MILITARY HARDWARE

OF WORLD WAR II

Steve Crawford

Brown
PARTWORKS

First published in 2000 by Brown Partworks Limited
8 Chapel Place
Rivington Street
London
EC2A 3DQ
UK

ISBN 1-84044-071-6

Editor: Peter Darman
Picture research: Antony Shaw
Design: Brown Partworks
Production: Matt Weyland

Printed in Hong Kong

Picture Credits
All photographs The Robert Hunt Library except:
TRH Pictures: 92
The Tank Museum Bovington: 264

CONTENTS

ARADO Ar 234 BLITZ

SPECIFICATIONS

ARADO Ar 234 BLITZ

Manufacturer: **Arado Flugzeugwerke**	Crew: **One**
Type: **Reconnaissance/Bomber**	Powerplant: **2 or 4 x Jumo turbojets**
Length: **12.65m (41ft 5.5in)**	Armament: **2 x MG 151 cannon**
Span: **14.40m (47ft 3.25in)**	Bomb load: **1500kg (3300lb)**
Height: **4.3m (14ft 1.25in)**	First flight: **15 June 1943**
Maximum speed: **780km/h (485mph)**	Initial climb: **Not Available**
Service ceiling: **16,370m (36,090ft)**	Weight (empty): **4800kg (10,580lb)**
Range: **2000km (1243 miles)**	Weight (loaded): **16,370m (36,090ft)**

The *Blitz* (Lightning) was the only turbojet-powered bomber to achieve operational status in World War II and is a milestone in military aviation's development. Its evolution dates from a 1940 requirement issued by the German Air Ministry (Luftfahrtministerium) for a fast reconnaissance aeroplane. An intensive programme of design and development resulted in no fewer than 18 prototypes, featuring a powerplant of two Junkers 004 or four BMW 003 turbojets, provision for rocket-assisted take-off units, a cabin with or without pressurization and an ejection seat, and a clumsy combination of a drop-away trolley for take-off and extendible skids for landing. A few of these prototypes were used from July 1944 by the reconnaissance units (Aufklärungsgruppe).

The production Ar 234B was intended for the reconnaissance bomber role with hardpoints under the fuselage and two engine nacelles for a 500kg (1100lb) bombload and utilized retractable tricycle landing gear in place of the trolley, an arrangement pioneered in the Ar 234 V9 prototype. Some 210 Ar 234B-1 reconnaissance aircraft with drop tanks in place of bombs and Ar 234B-2 reconnaissance bombers were built. The type entered service in September 1944, and was complemented by just 14 examples of the Ar 234C with the revised powerplant of four BMW 109-003A-1 turbojets.

ARADO Ar 95

Walter Blume designed the Arado Ar 95 in 1935 for the coastal patrol, reconnaissance and light attack role. It was a two-seat biplane with metallic fuselage and rear-folding wings. The wings had a metal structure, with the top one skinned in metal and the lower one in canvas. The prototype (Ar-95 V1) first flew during 1937, fitted with a Junkers Jumo V12 engine of 455kW (610hp).

Several prototypes tested successive modifications such as enlarged tail surfaces, a closed cockpit and a change to the 630kW (845hp) radial BMW 132 engine. The Ar-95 V3 was a three-seat version and the Ar-95 V4 had a fixed and spatted wheeled undercarriage. While the prototypes were still being tested, a pre-production run was started and several served in Spain with the Condor Legion. A small number were later in front-line Luftwaffe service early in the war before being relegated to training duties. The Ar-95A version had the BMW 132DC engine of 657kW (880hp) and a variable-pitch three-bladed propeller. The armament was a single fixed forward-firing MG15, mounted on the fuselage to fire through the propeller, and another MG15 on a flexible mounting to the rear. Under-fuselage it could carry a 700kg (1540lb) torpedo or a 375kg (825lb) bomb; under each wing 50kg (110lb) bombs. Chile bought six – three Ar 95A floatplanes and three wheeled-version Ar 95Bs.

SPECIFICATIONS

ARADO Ar 95A-1

Manufacturer: **Arado Flugzeugwerke**	Crew: **Two**
Type: **Coast Patrol, Light Attack**	Powerplant: **1 x BMW 132 radial**
Length: **11.10m (36ft 5in)**	Armament: **2 x 7.92mm MG15**
Span: **12.5m (41ft)**	Bomb load: **800kg (1760lb)**
Height: **3.60m (11ft 9.75in)**	First flight: **1937**
Maximum speed: **310km/h (193mph)**	Initial climb: **Not Available**
Service ceiling: **7300m (23,945ft)**	Weight (empty): **2450kg (5402lb)**
Range: **1100km (683 miles)**	Weight (loaded): **3560kg (7870lb)**

BLOHM UND VOSS Bv 141

SPECIFICATIONS

BLOHM UND VOSS Bv 141

Manufacturer: **Blohm und Voss**	Crew: **Three**
Type: **Tactical Reconnaissance**	Powerplant: **1 x BMW 801A radial**
Length: **13.95m (45ft 9.25in)**	Armament: **4 x 7.92mm MG**
Span: **17.46m (57ft 3.5in)**	Bomb load: **200kg (441lb)**
Height: **3.60m (11ft 9.75in)**	First flight: **25 February 1938**
Maximum speed: **438km/h (272mph)**	Initial climb: **Not Available**
Service ceiling: **10,000m (32,810ft)**	Weight (empty): **4700kg (10,362lb)**
Range: **1900km (1181 miles)**	Weight (loaded): **6100kg (13,448lb)**

In 1937 the Luftfahrtministerium (German Air Ministry) issued a requirement for a single-engined three-seat tactical reconnaissance aeroplane, drawing submissions from Focke Wulf in the form of its Fw 189, and Blohm und Voss's Bv 141 design. Much emphasis was placed on the need for good visibility, and in response the Bv 141 had a highly unusual asymmetric layout with the fully glazed crew nacelle offset to starboard of the centreline and a boom (carrying the engine at its front and a tail unit at its rear) offset to port.

The first of three prototypes flew in February 1938, and were evaluated at Erprobungstelle Rechlin with sufficient success to extract an order from the ministry for five Bv 141A-0 pre-production aircraft. Evaluation was completed successfully, but the type had poor performance as a result of its use of the 645kW (865hp) BMW 132N engine and so the next five aircraft were redesigned Bv 141B-0 machines with an uprated powerplant as well as a strengthened structure and a revised tail unit. These aircraft were used by the Aufklärungsschule 1 for service trials over the UK and the USSR from the autumn of 1941, but there were development delays because of persistent hydraulic problems and the programme was ended in 1943.

DORNIER Do 17

Designed as a fast mailplane (with single-fin tail surfaces) for Deutsche Lufthansa and first flown in 1934, the Do 17 was rejected by the airline and then developed by Dornier as a high-speed bomber with twin vertical tail surfaces. The aircraft entered service in early 1937, gaining the nickname "The Flying Pencil" on account of its slender rear fuselage. The first two military variants were the Do 17E-1 and Do 17F-1 for the high-speed bomber and long-range photo-reconnaissance roles respectively, the latter with additional fuel and the internal bomb bay revised to carry two cameras. The two types offered good performance and adequate all-round capabilities for their day, but by 1939 were obsolescent.

Progressive development led to the Do 17M/P medium bomber/reconnaissance aircraft and Do 17S/U reconnaissance/pathfinder types with liquid-cooled engines and a redesigned forward fuselage. The definitive model was the radial-engined Do 17Z of which 522 were built in three variants: the Do 17Z-1 with a 500kg (1102lb) bomb load, Do 17Z-2 with an uprated powerplant and load, and Do 17Z-3 reconnaissance bomber. Conversions included the Do 17Z-4 dual-control trainer, Do 17Z-5 maritime reconnaissance, Do 17Z-6 long-range night-fighter with the nose of the Ju Ju 88C-2, and Do 17Z-10 night-fighter with a redesigned nose.

SPECIFICATIONS

DORNIER Do 17

Manufacturer: **Dornier-Werke GmbH**	Crew: **Four**
Type: **medium bomber**	Powerplant: **2 x BMW Bramo radials**
Length: **15.80m (51ft 9.67in)**	Armament: **1 or 2 7.92mm MG**
Span: **18.00m (59ft 0.5in)**	Bomb load: **1000kg (2205lb)**
Height: **4.60m (15ft 1in)**	First flight: **Autumn 1934**
Maximum speed: **410km/h (255mph)**	Initial climb: **Not Available**
Service ceiling: **8200m (26,905ft)**	Weight (empty): **5200kg (11,464lb)**
Range: **1500km (932 miles)**	Weight (loaded): **8590kg (18,937lb)**

DORNIER Do 18

SPECIFICATIONS

DORNIER Do 18

Manufacturer: **Dornier-Werke GmbH**	Crew: **5/6**
Type: **Maritime Reconnaisance**	Powerplant: **2 x Jumo 205D diesels**
Length: **19.37m (63ft 7in)**	Armament: **1 x cannon, 1 x MG**
Span: **23.70m (77ft 9.25in)**	Bomb load: **100kg (220lb)**
Height: **5.32m (17ft 5.5in)**	First flight: **15 March 1935**
Maximum speed: **267km/h (166mph)**	Initial climb: **114m (374ft) per min**
Service ceiling: **4200m (13,780ft)**	Weight (empty): **5980kg (13,183lb)**
Range: **3500km (2175 miles)**	Weight (loaded): **10,800kg (23,809lb)**

The Do 18 was originally produced as a trans-Atlantic mail carrier to supersede the Dornier Wal 33 (from 1934 Do 15) in service with Deutsche Lufthansa on its South Atlantic routes, and later used as a medium-range maritime reconnaissance type by the Luftwaffe. The first of four prototypes made its maiden flight in March 1935, one of them being used for an experimental crossing of the North Atlantic. The twin-Junkers Jumo 205 diesels were mounted in tandem above the wing centre section, itself carried on a semi-circular hull with characteristic Dornier under-surface and lateral sponsons, and strengthened for catapulting (most German warships were equipped with catapults for mounting aircraft – vital for long-range reconnaissance).

Only six civil flying boats were completed, the majority of the approximately 148 production boats going to the military for service from 1938. The primary military variants were the Do 18D (three sub-variants to a total of about 75 machines) with 447.5kW (600hp) Junkers Jumo 205D Diesel engines, the Do 18G improved Do 18D with revised armament and provision for RATO units, and the Do 18H six-seat trainer. Do 18G and Do-18H production was 71 flying boats, and many Do 18G machines were converted to Do 18N standard as air-sea rescue flying boats.

DORNIER Do 217

The Do 217 was Dornier's response to a 1937 requirement for a long-range warplane optimized for the heavy level and dive-bombing roles, though later it was used in a variety of roles, even as a test bed for missile development. The Do 217 was in essence a scaled-up Do 215 version of the Do 17, and first flew in August 1938. The first operational model was the Do 217E of which some 800 aircraft were built in Do 217E-0 to Do 217E-4 sub-variants with BMW 801 radial engines. These were followed by the Do 217J, a night-fighter developed from the E which was structurally similar except for a redesigned solid armoured nose with a forward-firing armament comprising four 20mm MG FF cannon. It proved to be a potent aircraft.

Other variants were the Do 217K night bomber distinguished by a revised and unstepped nose, and finally the Do 217M development of the Do 217K with DB 603 inverted-Vee engines. Prototype and pre-production variants were the Do 217C bomber, Do 217P high-altitude reconnaissance, and Do 217R missile launching aircraft. There were also five Do 217E and two Do 217K sub-variants, notably the E-5 and K-2 (which had longer span wings), which were armed with Hs 293 anti-ship missiles and Fritz-X 1400 radio-corrected armour-piercing bombs respectively.

SPECIFICATIONS

DORNIER Do 217

Manufacturer: **Dornier-Werke GmbH**	*Crew:* **Four**
Type: **Heavy Bomber**	*Powerplant:* **2 x BMW 801ML radials**
Length: **18.20m (59ft 8.5in)**	*Armament:* **1 x cannon, 5 x MG**
Span: **19.00m (62ft 4in)**	*Bomb load:* **4000kg (8818lb)**
Height: **5.03m (16ft 6in)**	*First flight:* **August 1938**
Maximum speed: **515km/h (320mph)**	*Initial climb:* **216m (708ft) per min**
Service ceiling: **9000m (29,530ft)**	*Weight (empty):* **10,535kg (23,225lb)**
Range: **2800km (1740 miles)**	*Weight (loaded):* **16,465kg (36,299lb)**

FIESELER Fi 156 STORCH

SPECIFICATIONS

FIESELER Fi 156 STORCH

Manufacturer: **Gerhard Fieseler Werke**	Crew: **One**
Type: **Communications**	Powerplant: **1 x Argus inverted-Vee**
Length: **9.90m (32ft 5.75in)**	Armament: **1 x 7.92mm MG**
Span: **14.25m (46ft 9in)**	Bomb load: **Not Available**
Height: **3.05m (10ft)**	First flight: **March 1936**
Maximum speed: **175km/h (109mph)**	Initial climb: **286m (937ft) per min**
Service ceiling: **5200m (17,060ft)**	Weight (empty): **940kg (2072lb)**
Range: **1015km (631 miles)**	Weight (loaded): **1320kg (2910lb)**

The Fieseler Fi 156 *Storch* (Stork) was designed in response to a 1935 requirement issued by the Luftfahrtministerium for an army cooperation, casualty evacuation and liaison aeroplane. In prototype form it first flew in the spring of 1936 and entered service the following year. The ungainly but highly effective "Stork" was one of the most remarkable aircraft produced by the German aero industry during the Nazi regime. By incorporating innovative high-lift devices that he pioneered on pre-war acrobatic types, Gerhard Fieseler produced an aircraft with outstanding capability. This is borne out by some remarkable statistics: the Fi 156 Storch could take-off in 65m (213ft), land in 20m (66ft) and virtually hover in a 40km/h (25mph) wind without any loss of control.

Hitler's personal pilot used the exceptional STOL capability to land on an Alpine hotel terrace during the daring mountainside rescue of Benito Mussolini. Production totalled about 2900 aircraft, and the main variants were the initial, unarmed Fi 156A model, Fi-156C armed model in four main sub-variants, and Fi 156D air ambulance model in two sub-variants. The aircraft was held in high regard on both sides; at least three Allied generals are known to have used captured aircraft as their personal transportation.

FOCKE WULF Fw 189

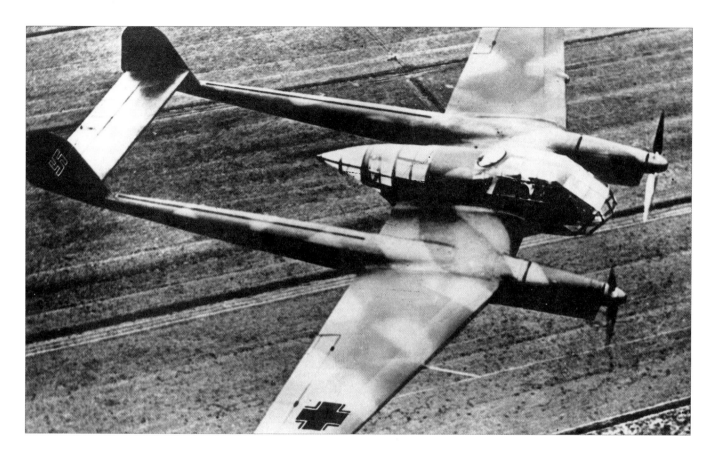

Despite its unusual appearance, which brought more than a few words of scepticism from conservative Luftwaffe pilots, the Fw 189 *Uhu* (Owl) was extremely effective in its intended role of army cooperation and short-range reconnaissance. It was only one of two such aircraft produced for the Luftwaffe – somewhat strangely considering it was designed primarily as a tactical air force for the support of the army. The prototype first flew in July 1938 – none of the subsequent prototype aircraft were alike – yet it was unknown by the Allies until it was disclosed in 1941 as the "Flying Eye" of German armies.

The aircraft was a twin-boom monoplane that accommodated the crew in an extensively glazed central nacelle. Service deliveries began in late 1940, and on the Eastern Front the aircraft performed beyond all expectations, retaining its superb handling and showing a remarkable ability to withstand damage and poor weather. Production totalled 848, excluding the 16 prototype and pre-production aircraft. The main model was the Fw 189A, produced in sub-variants such as the Fw 189A-1, Fw 189A-2 with twin rather than single defensive machine guns, Fw 189A-3 dual-control trainer, and Fw 189A-4 tactical support model with ventral armour and armed with a 20mm cannon rather than machine guns in the wing roots.

SPECIFICATIONS

FOCKE WULF Fw 189 UHU

Manufacturer: **Focke Wulf Flugzeugbau**	Crew: **Three**
Type: **Reconnaissance**	Powerplant: **2 x Argus As 410A-1**
Length: **12.03m (39ft 5.5in)**	Armament: **4 x 7.92mm MG**
Span: **18.40m (60ft 4.5in)**	Bomb load: **not available**
Height: **3.10m (10ft 2in)**	First flight: **July 1938**
Maximum speed: **350km/h (217mph)**	Initial climb: **485m (1590ft) per min**
Service ceiling: **7300m (23,950ft)**	Weight (empty): **3245kg (7154lb)**
Range: **670km (416 miles)**	Weight (loaded): **4170kg (9193lb)**

FOCKE WULF Fw 190

SPECIFICATIONS

FOCKE WULF Fw 190

Manufacturer:
Focke Wulf Flugzeugbau

Crew:
One

Type:
Single-seat Fighter

Powerplant:
1 x BMW 801D-2 radial

Length:
8.80m (28ft 10.5in)

Armament:
4 x cannon, 2 x MG

Span:
10.50m (34ft 5.5in)

Bomb load:
not available

Height:
3.95m (12ft 11.5in)

First flight:
1 June 1939

Maximum speed:
3.95m (12ft 11.5in)

Initial climb:
863m (2830ft) per min

Service ceiling:
10,600m (34,775ft)

Weight (empty):
2900kg (6393lb)

Range:
800km (497 miles)

Weight (loaded):
3980kg (8770lb)

This outstanding aircraft was in fact the only new fighter design to enter service with the Luftwaffe during the war. The prototype flew in June 1939 and after an intensive development programme in which both vee and radial engines were trialled, the Fw 190A entered production with a BMW 801 radial engine. The 40 Fw 190A-0 pre-production aircraft were followed by 100 Fw 190A-1 fighters, and the type entered service in the autumn of 1940. Although well known to the Allies prior to the war, the Fw 190 caused a nasty shock when it was first encountered over France in May 1941. It was light, manoeuvrable, fast, powerfully armed and immensely strong.

The A-1 was followed into service by the longer-span Fw 190A-2 with heavier armament, the Fw 190A-3 fighter-bomber with revised armament and Fw 190A-4 fighter-bombers with a methanol/water power boost system. There followed a profusion of different versions, and although the aircraft was substantially better than virtually all of the versions of the Spitfire, the Fw 190 never supplanted the Messerschmitt Bf 109 in production. As development of the aircraft progressed it was used increasingly in the fighter-bomber role and gained heavier armament, strengthened landing gear and numerous different engine fitments.

FOCKE WULF Fw 200

The Condor was designed as a transatlantic airliner for the German airline Deutsche Lufthansa. It first flew in prototype form during July 1937 and subsequently set up impressive record flights to New York and Tokyo, attracting export orders from Denmark, Brazil, Finland and Japan. The latter country ordered one aircraft for use as a long-range reconnaissance platform, and the resulting prototype attracted the attentions of the Luftwaffe, which put the aircraft into production.

The first of 259 Fw 200C military aircraft entered service in September 1939, and after the capitulation of France in 1940 they flew from bases along the Atlantic coast, searching for Allied convoys in the North Atlantic and then either attacking them directly with bombs and missiles or vectoring in packs of German U-boats. So effective were they in this role that Prime Minister Churchill labelled the Condor "the scourge of the Atlantic". A few aircraft were used as VIP transports (notably by Hitler and Himmler), but the majority of the machines were long-range reconnaissance bombers in seven sub-variants, some of which spawned their own sub-variants with different armament-fits, radar-fits and provision for missile-carriage and -guidance, as well as stripped-down forms for special transport tasks.

SPECIFICATIONS

FOCKE WULF Fw 200

Manufacturer: **Focke Wulf Flugzeugbau**	Crew: **Five**
Type: **Maritime Recon' Bomber**	Powerplant: **4 x BMW-Bramo 323R-2**
Length: **23.46m (76ft 11.5in)**	Armament: **1 x cannon, 4 x MG**
Span: **32.84m (107ft 8in)**	Bomb load: **2100kg (4630lb)**
Height: **6.30m (20ft 8in)**	First flight: **not given**
Maximum speed: **360km/h (224mph)**	Initial climb: **not available**
Service ceiling: **6000m (19,685ft)**	Weight (empty): **12,950kg (28,549lb)**
Range: **4440km (2759 miles)**	Weight (loaded): **22,700kg (50,044lb)**

GOTHA Go 242 and 244

SPECIFICATIONS

GOTHA Go 242 AND 244

Manufacturer: **Gotha Waggonfabrik**	Crew: **Two**
Type: **Troop Transporter**	Powerplant: **2 x Gnome-Rhône radial**
Length: **15.80m (51ft 10.25in)**	Armament: **4 x 7.92mm MG**
Span: **24.50m (80ft 4.5in)**	Bomb load: **Not Available**
Height: **4.60m (15ft 1in)**	First flight: **Not Given**
Maximum speed: **290km/h (180mph)**	Initial climb: **270m (885ft) per min**
Service ceiling: **7650m (25,100ft)**	Weight (empty): **5225kg (11,517lb)**
Range: **740km (460 miles)**	Weight (loaded): **7800kg (17,196lb)**

Well known as a producer of bomber aircraft for the German Air Service during World War I, Gotha re-entered aircraft production in 1936 and after the outbreak of war devoted its attentions to the design and manufacture of military aircraft. The most successful of its wartime designs was the Go 242, a high-wing twin-boom monoplane with a central nacelle that could accommodate 23 fully equipped troops. Introduced into service in 1942, the Go 242 subsequently became the Luftwaffe's standard transport glider, with deliveries totalling 1526 Go 242A and Go 242B gliders with skid and wheeled landing gear respectively.

Typically, the aircraft were towed by Ju 52 or He 111 aircraft, and were used during the daring airborne invasion of Crete in May 1941. The Go 242 was designed with a view to the installation of engines, and its success paved the way for the Go 244, which was powered with French engines. Deliveries totalled 174 aircraft, including 133 converted Go 242B gliders. Of this latter type there were five versions: the Go 244B-1 freighter with torsion-bar shock absorption, Go 244B-2 freighter with wider track main units and oleo shock absorption, Go 244B-3 and B-4 paratroop transport versions of the Go 244B-1 and B-2, and Go 244B-5 with dual controls and balanced rudders.

HEINKEL He 60

O ne of the last of the many floatplanes designed by Ernst Heinkel was the He 60, a two-seat biplane powered by a BMW vee engine. This was intended for catapult operations from the decks of the larger German warships, and first flew in 1933 in prototype form. The 492kW (660hp) BMW V1 engine was subsequently replaced in the second He 60B prototype by a 559kW (750hp) version of the same engine, but this offered no significant improvement and was not adopted for subsequent aircraft. The third He 60c prototype had catapult launching equipment and underwent a series of trials that confirmed its suitability for operational use.

The first production He 60B aircraft entered service with training units in 1933 and as the programme of rebuilding Germany's navy accelerated, the type was selected for service aboard German battle cruisers and cruisers. In 1934 an improved version (He 60C) was introduced. The aircraft saw extensive service in the Spanish Civil War, where it performed well. By the time that war had broken out in Europe at the beginning of September 1939, however, the He 60 was fast becoming obsolete and it was soon relegated to training duties only, although German maritime reconnaissance units based in Greece and Crete continued to operate the He 60 until 1943.

SPECIFICATIONS

HEINKEL He 60

Manufacturer: **Ernst Heinkel A.G**	Crew: **Two**
Type: **Reconnaissance Seaplane**	Powerplant: **1 x BMW VI 6.0ZU**
Length: **11.48m (37ft 8in)**	Armament: **2 x MG**
Span: **13.5m (44ft 3in)**	Bomb load: **None**
Height: **N/A**	First flight: **1933**
Maximum speed: **225km/h (140mph)**	Initial climb: **N/A**
Service ceiling: **5000m (16,400ft)**	Weight (empty): **N/A**
Range: **720km (447 miles)**	Weight (loaded): **N/A**

HEINKEL He 111

SPECIFICATIONS

HEINKEL HE 111

Manufacturer: **Ernst Heinkel A.G.**	Crew: **4/5**
Type: **Medium Bomber**	Powerplant: **2 x Junkers Jumo 211F-2**
Length: **16.40m (53ft 9.5in)**	Armament: **7 x 7.92mm MG**
Span: **22.60m (74ft 1.75in)**	Bomb load: **2500kg (5511lb)**
Height: **3.40m (13ft 1.5in)**	First flight: **24 February 1935**
Maximum speed: **405km/h (252mph)**	Initial climb: **170m (558ft) per min**
Service ceiling: **8500m (27,890ft)**	Weight (empty): **8680kg (19,136lb)**
Range: **1930km (1199 miles)**	Weight (loaded): **14,000kg (30,865lb)**

The Heinkel He 111 was the natural twin-engined outgrowth of the Heinkel 70 bomber used to such great effect in Spain. Although revealed to the world as a civil airliner, it was designed for bombing. Powered by twin BMW VI engines, it could carry 1000kg (2205lb) of bombs stowed nose-up in eight cells in the centre section. In 1937 some similar machines flew secret reconnaissance missions over Britain, France and the Soviet Union in the guise of airliners, and in the same year the He 111B-1 entered service with the Luftwaffe. In February 1937 operations began with the Condor Legion in Spain, where its seeming invincibility led many to become complacent.

The 300 He 111B-1s were followed by 190 He 111E bombers with Junkers Jumo 211 engines. The next significant model, in spring 1939, was the He 111P with the asymmetric fully glazed nose typical of all subsequent models. Some 400 aircraft were built in six sub-variants (He 111P-1 to He 111P-6). The definitive model was the He 111H (6150 built in 23 sub-variants). Development was characterized by a progressively uprated powerplant, increased fuel capacity, improved defensive and offensive armament, additional armour protection and provision for use in alternative roles: anti-shipping, pathfinding, missile platform, paratroop-delivery and glider-towing.

HEINKEL He 112

One of the first requirements issued under the Nazis by the rapidly expanded Reichsluftfahrtministerium was a specification for a monoplane fighter to replace the Arado 68 and Heinkel 51. Designed by a Heinkel team under Walter Günthers (who was also responsible for the He 70), the He 112 was Heinkel's entry to the competition.

The Heinkel was comparatively advanced, and the first of an eventual 12 prototypes flew in the summer of 1935. During the programme a number of powerplant, fuselage, wing and tail unit configurations were investigated. The Luftwaffe then selected the Bf 109, but the German Air Ministry was sufficiently impressed with the Heinkel to order 43 He 112B-0 pre-production aircraft that operated with a fighter wing during 1938. Seventeen of the aircraft were sent to Spain to fight in the Civil War (not as part of the Condor Legion, but flown instead by civilian volunteers), after which the 15 survivors were passed to the Spanish Nationalist forces. Of the others, Germany sold 13 each to Japan and Romania, the latter subsequently also acquiring 11 of the 13 He 112B-1 production aircraft for service up to 1942, notably during the invasion of the Soviet Union in June 1941. Hungary also acquired a few aircraft.

SPECIFICATIONS

HEINKEL He 112

Manufacturer:
Ernst Heinkel A.G.

Type:
Fighter, Ground-Attack

Length:
9.30m (30ft 6in)

Span:
9.10m (29ft 10.25in)

Height:
3.85m (12ft 7.5in)

Maximum speed:
510km/h (317mph)

Service ceiling:
8500m (27,890ft)

Range:
1100km (683 miles)

Crew:
One

Powerplant:
1 x Junkers Jumo 210Ea

Armament:
2 x cannon, 2 x MG

Bomb load:
60kg (132lb)

First flight:
September 1935

Initial climb:
700m (2,300ft) per min

Weight (empty):
1620kg (3571lb)

Weight (loaded):
2250kg (4960lb)

HENSCHEL Hs 126

SPECIFICATIONS

HENSCHEL Hs 126

Manufacturer: **Henschel Flugzeug-Werke**	Crew: **Two**
Type: **Reconnaissance**	Powerplant: **1 x BMW-Bramo 323A-1**
Length: **10.85m (35ft 7in)**	Armament: **2 x 7.92mm MG**
Span: **14.50m (47ft 6.75in)**	Bomb load: **150kg (331lb)**
Height: **3.75m (12ft 3.5in)**	First flight: **autumn 1936**
Maximum speed: **355km/h (221mph)**	Initial climb: **not given**
Service ceiling: **8230m (27,000ft)**	Weight (empty): **2032kg (4480lb)**
Range: **720km (447 miles)**	Weight (loaded): **3270kg (7209lb)**

A development of the earlier Hs 122 trainer and light reconnaissance aircraft of 1934, the Hs 126 provided the Germans with the bulk of their battlefield reconnaissance capability in World War II. It gained a new wing, cantilever main landing gear and a canopy over the pilot's cockpit, which were fitted to an Hs 122 airframe to produce the Junkers Jumo 210-powered prototype that first flew in autumn 1936. This was followed by two development aircraft powered by a Bramo Fafnir 323A-1 and 10 Hs 126A-0 pre-production, some of which were evaluated by German forces fighting alongside the Nationalists in the Spanish Civil War.

These aircraft paved the way for about 800 examples of the two production variants, the first of which entered service during 1938 with Aufklärungsgruppe 35. These models were the Hs 126A-1 with the 656kW (880hp) BMW 132Dc radial engine, and the Hs 126B-1 fitted with a different engine. The Hs 126 served in a front-line role through to 1942, when they began to be replaced by the Focke Wulf Fw 189, and were thereafter relegated to the glider-towing and night harassment roles, the latter with light bomb loads in regions such as the Baltic and Balkans. The Greek Air Force also received 16 examples of the type, which continued in service beyond the end of World War II.

HENSCHEL Hs 129

Designed by Henschel in response to a requirement in spring 1937 for a twin-engine ground-attack aircraft, to provide close air support for ground forces, that could carry at least two 20mm cannon and extensive protection, the Hs 129 was a cantilever low-wing monoplane of all-metal construction and it first flew in spring 1939 with two 347kW (465hp) Argus As 410 inverted-Vee engines. Poor performance hampered development, which was further hindered when the Luftwaffe pilots who tested the prototypes complained about poor fields of vision and sluggish handling. This forced Henschel to undertake a radical series of improvements that resulted in the Hs 129B-1.

In April 1942 this type entered service with captured French radial engines. It was still underpowered, and the engines were both unreliable and vulnerable, but the demands of the Eastern Front resulted in the delivery of 843 Hs 129Bs. The Hs 129B-2, introduced in 1943, incorporated provision for under-fuselage attachments for anti-tank weapons. Sub-variants had cannons whose installation meant the deletion of the machine guns to provide room for the cannon's ammunition, and some 25 Hs 129B-2 warplanes were adapted on the production line with a 75mm BK 7,5 (converted PaK 40L) anti-tank gun in a jettisonable under-fuselage pack.

SPECIFICATIONS

HENSCHEL Hs 129

Manufacturer:
Henschel Flugzeug-Werke

Type:
Close-Support, Anti-Tank

Length:
9.75m (31ft 11.75in)

Span:
14.20m (46ft 7in)

Height:
3.25m (10ft 8in)

Maximum speed:
407km/h (253mph)

Service ceiling:
9000m (29,530ft)

Range:
560km (348 miles)

Crew:
One

Powerplant:
2 x Gnome-Rhône radial

Armament:
2 x cannon, 2 x MG

Bomb load:
450kg (992lb)

First flight:
Spring 1939

Initial climb:
486m (1595ft) per min

Weight (empty):
4020kg (8862lb)

Weight (loaded):
5250kg (11,574lb)

JUNKERS Ju 52

SPECIFICATIONS

JUNKERS Ju 52

Manufacturer: **Junkers Flugzeug**	Crew: **Three**
Type: **Transport**	Powerplant: **3 x BMW 132T-2 radial**
Length: **18.90m (62ft)**	Armament: **4 x 7.92mm MG**
Span: **29.20m (95ft 10in)**	Bomb load: **Not Available**
Height: **4.52m (14ft 10in)**	First flight: **13 October 1930**
Maximum speed: **286km/h (178mph)**	Initial climb: **171m (562ft) per min**
Service ceiling: **5900m (19,360ft)**	Weight (empty): **6500kg (14,328lb)**
Range: **1305km (811 miles)**	Weight (loaded): **11,030kg (24,317lb)**

The "Tante Ju" (Auntie Ju) was the main workhorse of the Luftwaffe transport units for the duration of the war. It was intended as a replacement for the highly successful W 33 and W 34 transports of 1927, and planned from that time as an enlarged version of the same basic design concept with the stressed, corrugated metal skin characteristic of Junkers aircraft. It first flew in prototype form during October 1930 with one 541kW (725hp) BMW VII Vee engine. The Ju 52a to Ju 52d initial production models for the civil market differed only in the type of engine used, but with the Ju 52/3m a three-engined powerplant was introduced for greater payload and performance. Most early Ju 52/3m versions were 15- to 17-seat passenger airliners which sold all over the world, at one time making up 75 per cent of the Lufthansa fleet.

In 1935 the Ju 52/3mg3e bomber, with manually aimed MG 15s in a dorsal cockpit and ventral dustbin, and a bomb load of 1500kg (3307lb) equipped the first Luftwaffe bombing squadron, but nearly all of the 4850 aircraft built – the vast majority of them to meet military orders in variants between the Ju 52/3m ge and the Ju 52/3mg14e – were equipped as troop transports, freighters and casualty evacuation aircraft. During World War II it was used in every theatre through to May 1945.

JUNKERS Ju 87

Newsreels of Ju 87 Stuka dive-bombers peeling off to begin their near vertical attacks are some of the most familiar images of the war. The Ju 87 was planned as a Stuka (short for Sturzkampfluzeug, or "dive-bomber") a name that became synonymous with the type, to provide 'flying artillery' to support the armoured forces that would spearhead Germany's Blitzkrieg (lightning war) tactics, and is forever associated with the success of that strategy early in the war. The aircraft first flew in 1935 with twin vertical tail surfaces and a British Rolls-Royce (RR) Kestrel engine, but was then developed into the Ju 87A initial production model (200 aircraft) with a single vertical surface, the 507kW (680hp) Junkers Jumo 210 inverted-Vee engine, trousered landing gear (to improve the aerodynamic efficiency of the no-retracting undercarriage) and a crutch to swing the bomb away from the fuselage before release.

The Ju 87A entered service in spring 1937 but was soon supplanted by the Ju 87B-1, which had a much uprated powerplant. In Poland the Stuka proved devastating; less than a year later its vulnerability was exposed over southern England. Many sub-variants were produced until 1944; from 1942 to 1945 its main work was close-support and attacking armour on the Eastern Front, although it was also used as a transport and glider tug.

SPECIFICATIONS

JUNKERS Ju 87

Manufacturer: **Junkers Flugzeug**	Crew: **Two**
Type: **Dive-Bomber**	Powerplant: **1 x Junkers Jumo 211Da**
Length: **1.10m (36ft 5in)**	Armament: **3 x 7.92mm MG**
Span: **13.80m (45ft 3.33in)**	Bomb load: **1000kg (2205lb)**
Height: **4.01m (13ft 2in)**	First flight: **November 1935**
Maximum speed: **383km/h (238mph)**	Initial climb: **462m (1515ft) per min**
Service ceiling: **8000m (26,245ft)**	Weight (empty): **2710kg (5974lb)**
Range: **790km (491 miles)**	Weight (loaded): **4340kg (9568lb)**

JUNKERS Ju 88

SPECIFICATIONS

JUNKERS Ju 88

Manufacturer: **Junkers Flugzeug**	Crew: **Four**
Type: **High-Speed Bomber**	Powerplant: **2 x Junkers Jumo 211J**
Length: **14.40m (47ft 2.75in)**	Armament: **7 x 7.92mm MG**
Span: **20m (65ft 7.5in)**	Bomb load: **2500kg (5511lb)**
Height: **4.85m (15ft 11in)**	First flight: **21 December 1936**
Maximum speed: **470km/h (292mph)**	Initial climb: **235m (770ft) per min**
Service ceiling: **8200m (26,900ft)**	Weight (empty): **9860kg (21,737lb)**
Range: **2730km (1696 miles)**	Weight (loaded): **14,000kg (30,865lb)**

Probably no other aircraft in history has been developed in so many different forms for so many purposes as the Ju 88, with the possible exception of Britain's Mosquito. The Ju 88 was flown in 1936 as a civil prototype, and it remained of vital importance to Germany throughout the war. After a frantic design process led by two Americans well versed in modern stressed skin construction, it was transformed into a heavier, slower and more capacious high-speed level- and dive-bomber of the type just then entering service when war broke out. Structurally the aircraft was excellent, combining a large internal fuel capacity with great load-carrying capability, and despite the fact that many of its variants were mere "lash-ups", the performance of the aircraft was never so degraded as to become seriously vulnerable – as the Dornier and Heinkel bombers were.

The most important early model was the Ju 88A, of which some 7000 or more were delivered in variants up to the Ju 88A-17 with steadily uprated engines, enhanced defensive armament and improved offensive capability. The final total of 15,000 Ju 88s of all models gives an idea of the significance of this aircraft, which as well as its bombing role was also developed to serve as a night-fighter, close-support and big-gun anti-armour machine, and missile-carrying reconnaissance platform.

MESSERSCHMITT
Bf 109

The Bf 109 was the standard Luftwaffe fighter of the war, with more than 30,500 examples built before and during it. Willy Messerschmitt began work on this classic machine in 1935, in response to Germany's requirement for its first "modern" monoplane fighter (see Heinkel He 112). It was revealed in September 1935, when the first of 13 prototypes flew. The Bf 109B entered service in April 1937 and was followed by the Bf 109C with extra guns. Both saw service in the Spanish Civil War. They were followed by the Bf 109D and the Bf 109E ("Emil"), which entered service at the end of 1938 and was Germany's standard single-seat fighter at the start of World War II – instrumental in Luftwaffe successes over Poland, Scandinavia and the Low Countries.

Only when it took part in the Battle of Britain were its limitations realized. Predictably, the Bf 109 was developed into many variants – when standardization would have benefited the war effort. Engines, armament, nose profiles, cockpit hoods, modified flying services and the like were all refined in attempts to maintain combat proficiency. The most numerous variant (23,500) was the Bf 109G, but few of those who flew it would dispute that improvements in the type's speed and firepower – gained by the introduction of the more powerful DB 605 engine – resulted in poorer overall handling qualities.

SPECIFICATIONS

MESSERSCHMITT Bf 109

Manufacturer:
Messerschmitt A.G

Type:
Fighter, Fighter-Bomber

Length:
8.85m (29ft 0.5in)

Span:
9.92m (32ft 6.5in)

Height:
2.50m (8ft 2.5in)

Maximum speed:
621km/h (386mph)

Service ceiling:
11,550m (37,890ft)

Range:
1000km (621 miles)

Crew:
One

Powerplant:
1 x DB 605

Armament:
1 x cannon, 2 x MG

Bomb load:
250kg (551lb)

First flight:
Late 1935

Initial climb:
950m (3116ft) per min

Weight (empty):
2673kg (5893lb)

Weight (loaded):
3400kg (7496lb)

MESSERSCHMITT Bf 110

SPECIFICATIONS

MESSERSCHMITT Bf 110

Manufacturer: **Messerschmitt A.G**	Crew: **2/3**
Type: **Heavy Fighter**	Powerplant: **2 x DB 601A-1**
Length: **12.10m (39ft 8.33in)**	Armament: **1 x cannon, 5 x MG**
Span: **16.20m (53ft 1.8in)**	Bomb load: **Not Available**
Height: **4.13m (13ft 6.5in)**	First flight: **2 May 1936**
Maximum speed: **560km/h (248mph)**	Initial climb: **585m (1755ft) per min**
Service ceiling: **10,000m (32,810ft)6**	Weight (empty): **5150kg (11,354lb**
Range: **1095km (680 miles)**	Weight (loaded): **6750kg (14,881lb)**

During the 1930s air strategists believed twin-engine "heavy fighters" to be essential to offensive air operations. As was happening elsewhere at the same time, in 1934 the Reichsluftfahrtministerium issued a requirement for a machine capable of tackling aircraft, including single-seat fighters, sent up to intercept the bombers; it was to make up in firepower what it lacked in manoeuvrability and was dubbed *Zerstörer* (destroyer). Messerschmitt's prototype Bf 110V1 first flew in May 1936 and the production Bf 110 entered service as the Bf 110B with two 700hp (522kW) Junkers Jumo 210 engines. Only 45 were built before the advent of the Bf 110C with two Daimler-Benz DB 601 engines, which had seven sub-variants, and the Bf 110D, built in three.

Pitched against smaller, lighter fighter aircraft during the Battle of Britain, the Bf 110 proved vulnerable and from autumn 1940 production of the indifferent Bf 110C/D was scaled down. In spring 1941 two new variants, the -E (light bomber) and -F, appeared. The Bf 110F was introduced to take advantage of the powerful new DB 601F engine, and as the F-4 night-fighter got early Lichtenstein radar equipment. With later night versions -G and -H, in 1944 the Bf 110 represented 60 per cent of the strength of the Luftwaffe night-fighter units. By March 1945 a total of 6050 Bf 110s had been built.

MESSERSCHMITT 323

Originally planned as a heavy tank and troop transport glider, and first flown on 25 February 1941, the Me 321 V1 prototype had a single-crew member and a substantial cargo hold that could accommodate some 200 troops or 20,000kg (44,092lb) of freight. The Me 321A-1 entered service in late in 1941, followed by the Me 321B-1 with a crew of three and two defensive machine-guns. Luftwaffe transport pilots found that the Me 321 handled adequately in the air, but lacked a suitably powerful tug (even the extraordinary five-engined Heinkel He 111Z proved inadequate). This led to further development as the Me 323 with multi-wheel landing gear, structural strengthening and six Gnome-Rhône radial engines from captured French stocks.

The initial production variant was the Me 323D-1 with the ability to carry a payload of 9750kg (21,495lb), including 120 troops or 60 litters, over a range of 1000km (621 miles). Deliveries began in August 1942, and in November of the same year the Me 323Ds were put to work supplying Rommel's beleaguered Afrika Korps across the Mediterranean. The lumbering giant proved easy pickings for Allied pilots and heavy losses were suffered. Later models included the Me 323E, with stronger structure, greater fuel capacity and heavier defensive armament.

SPECIFICATIONS

MESSERSCHMITT 323

Manufacturer: **Messerschmitt A.G**	Crew: **10/11**
Type: **Heavy Transport**	Powerplant: **6 x Gnome-Rhône radials**
Length: **28.5m (93ft 6in)**	Armament: **1 x 20mm; 5 x MG**
Span: **55m (180ft 5.33in)**	Bomb load: **None**
Height: **9.6m (31ft 6in)**	First flight: **1942**
Maximum speed: **253km/h (157mph)**	Initial climb: **N/A**
Service ceiling: **4500m (14,760ft)**	Weight (empty): **29,600kg (65,256lb)**
Range: **1300km (808 miles)**	Weight (loaded): **45,000kg (99,206lb)**

MESSERSCHMITT Me 410

SPECIFICATIONS

MESSERSCHMITT Me 410

Manufacturer:
Messerschmitt A.G

Type:
Heavy Fighter

Length:
12.48m (40ft 11.5in)

Span:
16.35m (53ft 7.75in)

Height:
4.28m (14ft 0.5in)

Maximum speed:
624km/h (388mph)

Service ceiling:
10,000m (32,810ft)

Range:
1670km (1050 miles)

Crew:
Two

Powerplant:
2 x DB 603A

Armament:
4 x cannon, 4 x MG

Bomb load:
Not Available

First flight:
1942

Initial climb:
628m (2060ft) per min

Weight (empty):
7518kg (16,574lb)

Weight (loaded):
10,650kg (23,483lb)

In 1937 Messerschmitt began developing the Bf 210, planned as a more versatile successor to the Bf 110. In June 1939 an order for 1000 aircraft was placed "off the drawing board", but after prototype Me 210V1 had revealed flight instability and landing gear problems, progress foundered. Production aircraft were delivered from late 1941 but in service it was a complete flop and production ended after 352 machines. The failure of the Me 210 nearly cost Willy Messerschmitt his job. Key aspects of the design were changed to produce the Me 410, which proved to be an altogether more capable as well as more successful warplane. The Me 210's failings had in fact been solved just before its cancellation, and it was from this type that the Me 410 was evolved, with basically the same revised aerodynamic and structural features in combination with modified outer wing panels and the different powerplant of two Daimler-Benz DB 603A inverted-Vee piston engines. The Me 410 first flew in prototype form in autumn 1942, and there followed 1137 production aircraft in variants such as the Me 410A (three major variants) and the Me 410B. Five major variants of the 410B were produced with the DB 603G engines. The B-5 anti-shipping torpedo bomber, the B-7 day reconnaissance and B-8 night reconnaissance aircraft were still in the experimental stage at the war's end.

AVRO ANSON

During a production run that lasted from 1934 to 1952, this ubiquitous aircraft was built in larger numbers than any other British aeroplane except the Hawker Hurricane and Supermarine Spitfire. The Anson was initially conceived as a light transport for Imperial Airways and entered service with the carrier as the Avro 652 in March 1936. The design was also adapted to 652A standard with a dorsal turret and square rather then round windows, to meet an Air Ministry specification issued in May 1934 that called for a twin-engined landplane to be used in the coastal reconnaissance role.

The prototype first flew in March 1935, and the type was ordered into production as the Anson Mk I (later Anson GR.Mk I) with other minor modifications to the tail unit, and powered by 250kW (335hp) Armstrong Siddeley Cheetah IX radial seven-cylinder, single-row radial engines (later aircraft received uprated 295kW/-395hp Cheetah XIX engines).

The first of these aircraft flew in December 1935, and the type entered service in March of the following year at the start of a programme that saw the delivery of 6915 aircraft. As well as its coastal reconnaissance role, the Anson was also adapted for use as an advanced flying, navigation and gunnery trainer and also for use as a communications aircraft.

SPECIFICATIONS

AVRO ANSON

Manufacturer: **A.V. Roe & Co., Ltd.**	Crew: **3/4**
Type: **Coastal Reconnaisance**	Powerplant: **2 x Cheetah IX**
Length: **12.88m (42ft 3in)**	Armament: **4 x 0.303in MG**
Span: **17.22m (56ft 6in))**	Bomb load: **227kg (500lb)**
Height: **3.99m (13ft 1in)**	First flight: **March 1935**
Maximum speed: **303km/h (188mph)**	Initial climb: **293m (960ft) per min**
Service ceiling: **5790m (19,000ft)**	Weight (empty): **2438kg (5375lb)**
Range: **1271 km (790km)**	Weight (loaded): **4218kg (9300lb)**

AVRO LANCASTER

SPECIFICATIONS

AVRO LANCASTER

Manufacturer: **A.V. Roe & Co., Ltd.**	Crew: **Seven**
Type: **Heavy Bomber**	Powerplant: **4 x RR Merlin XX**
Length: **21.18m (69ft 6in)**	Armament: **9 x 0.303in MG**
Span: **31.09m (102ft 0in)**	Bomb load: **8165kg (18,000lb)**
Height: **6.25m (20ft 6in)**	First flight: **9 January 1941**
Maximum speed: **462km/h (287mph)**	Initial climb: **76m (250ft) per min**
Service ceiling: **5790m (19,000ft)**	Weight (empty): **16,783kg (37,000lb)**
Range: **2784km (1730 miles)**	Weight (loaded): **29,484kg (65,000lb)**

The most successful heavy night bomber used by the Royal Air Force in World War II, the Lancaster was a development of the underpowered Manchester with the revised powerplant of four Rolls-Royce (RR) Merlin 12-cylinder Vee engines. The Lancaster first flew on 9 January 1941 and entered service from the beginning of 1942. It soon developed a reputation as a sturdy aeroplane that handled well in the air, possessed moderately good performance, and had good defensive and offensive firepower. The fact that the design was "right" from the beginning is reflected by the very small number of changes made during the course of a long production run that covered 10 variants.

The demand for Merlin engines soon outgrew Rolls-Royce's production capacity, resulting in the decision to use the American licence-built version, namely the Packard V-1650 in its Merlin 28, 38 or 224 forms. Installed in the Lancaster Mk I, the aeroplane was known as the Lancaster Mk III (later B.Mk III and finally B.Mk 3) and was also produced in Canada by Victory Aircraft Ltd. of Toronto. Special versions were built for the carrying of the bouncing bombs used on the famous raids against the Ruhr Dams and for dropping deep-penetration-type bombs (5443kg/12,000lb "Tallboy" and 9979kg/22,000lb "Grand Slam".)

AVRO LINCOLN

The third outgrowth of the Manchester was the Type 694 Lincoln, designed to British Air Ministry Specification B14/43 as the replacement for the Lancaster. Originally known as the Lancaster IV, and resembling its more famous brother, the new aircraft was intended to fly farther and higher, gaining a new wing, longer fuselage, heavier armament and stronger landing gear. H2S radar was fitted as standard.

The first unarmed prototype flew in June 1944, later gaining a Martin dorsal turret. The second prototype flew in November 1944 with a Bristol dorsal turret, this being the definitive form for production aircraft. The first production machines were delivered in February 1945 but although plans for mass production by three manufacturers had been laid, production was scaled down after VE Day in May 1945 and totalled only 72 Mk Is and 465 Mk IIs. Bomber Command squadrons began to take delivery in August, some months later than originally scheduled and too late for the Lincoln to see operational service in World War II.

The Lincoln remained in Royal Air Force service until replaced by the Canberra in the early 1950s. This great family of Avro aircraft found its ultimate realization in the Shackleton, which served with the Royal Air Force until the mid-1980s.

SPECIFICATIONS

AVRO LINCOLN

Manufacturer: **A.V. Roe & Co. Ltd.**	Crew: **Seven**
Type: **Heavy Bomber**	Powerplant: **4 x RR Merlin 85**
Length: **23.86m (78ft 3.5in)**	Armament: **6 x 0.50in MG**
Span: **36.58m (120ft)**	Bomb load: **6350kg (14,000lb)**
Height: **5.27m (17ft 3.5in)**	First flight: **9 June 1944**
Maximum speed: **475km/h (295mph)**	Initial climb: **Not Available**
Service ceiling: **9295m (30,500ft)**	Weight (empty): **19,686kg (43,400lb)**
Range: **2366km (1470 miles)**	Weight (loaded): **34,019kg (75,000lb)**

AVRO MANCHESTER

SPECIFICATIONS

AVRO MANCHESTER

Manufacturer: **A.V. Roe & Co. Ltd.**	Crew: **Seven**
Type: **Medium Bomber**	Powerplant: **2 x RR Vulture X-type**
Length: **21.14m (69ft 4.25in)**	Armament: **8 x 0.303in MG**
Span: **27.46m (90ft 1in)**	Bomb load: **4695kg (10,350lb)**
Height: **5.94m (19ft 6in)**	First flight: **25 July 1939**
Maximum speed: **426km/h (265mph)**	Initial climb: **Not Available**
Service ceiling: **5850m (19,200ft)**	Weight (empty): **13,350kg (29,432lb)**
Range: **2623km (1630 miles)**	Weight (loaded): **25,402kg (56,000lb)**

During the inter-war period the Air Ministry concentrated much of its resources on building up a fleet of bombers, in line with the doctrine of the day on future offensive air operations. In 1936 the ministry issued a requirement that elicited responses from both Avro and Handley Page. Both companies received prototype orders although the Handley Page H.P 56 did not progress beyond the drawing board (the company preferring instead to focus on development of the Halifax), thus allowing a clear field for the Avro design.

The first of two Manchester prototypes flew in July 1939, after an initial order for 200 aircraft had been placed to the revised 19/37 Specification. Following flight trials the wing span was increased by 3m (10ft) and a central fin was added. The Manchester Mk I became operational in November 1940 with No 207 Squadron at Waddington, and these 20 aircraft were followed by 180 examples of the Manchester Mk IA with larger endplate vertical surfaces on the tail, allowing the removal of the Mk I's centreline surface. In service the Manchester was a failure; despite having an ideal airframe, the twin Vulture did not provide sufficient power and was wholly unreliable. By the time that the Manchester was retired in June 1942, 40 per cent of the 202 aircraft had been lost on operations and another 25 per cent had crashed.

AVRO YORK

During the war, RAF Transport Command was supplied with American aircraft, under a contract that freed the British aircraft industry to concentrate on fighter and bomber production. Avro designers under Roy Chadwick nevertheless went ahead with the design of a four-engine long-range passenger and cargo transport aircraft, a process which they completed in February 1942. The new aircraft mated the wings, tail assembly, engines and landing gear with a new fuselage of roughly rectangular section fitted with large hatches to enable bulky items to be loaded. After the first flight in July 1942, an official order was placed for four aircraft. The third aircraft against this order gained a third fin to compensate for the additional side area of the forward fuselage and in this form was delivered to the RAF as the York I from March 1943.

This was the first of a number of aircraft that were fitted out for VIP transport duties and in the ensuing months carried such dignitaries as King George VI and Prime Minister Winston Churchill across the globe. With Avro fully occupied with the production of Lancaster bombers, only a small number of Yorks were built before 1944, when the aircraft was put into mass production. Some 257 were built in all and eventually 10 RAF squadrons were equipped with the type.

SPECIFICATIONS

AVRO YORK

Manufacturer: **A.V. Roe & Co. Ltd.**	Crew: **Four**
Type: **Long-Range Transport**	Powerplant: **4 x RR Merlin XX**
Length: **23.93m (78ft 6in)**	Armament: **None**
Span: **31.09m (102ft 6in)**	Bomb load: **None**
Height: **5.44m (17ft 10in)**	First flight: **5 July 1942**
Maximum speed: **480km/h (298mph)**	Initial climb: **Not Available**
Service ceiling: **7010m (23,000ft)**	Weight (empty): **19,069kg (42,040lb)**
Range: **4345km (2700 miles)**	Weight (loaded): **31,115kg (68,597lb)**

SHORT STIRLING

Although in appearance an extremely impressive aircraft, with vast length, unprecedented height and even two separate tailwheels, the Stirling was unpopular with the men who flew it. The design was completed in 1938 to Specification B.12/36, which called for a seven/eight-man crew heavy bomber. The prototype flew in May 1939, and in August 1940 the first production aircraft began to be delivered, marking the entry into service of the first four-engined heavy bomber for RAF Bomber Command. The Air Ministry's demand for a span of less than 30.48m (100ft) meant that in service the Stirling suffered from poor ceiling and sluggish manoeuvrability. Although it carried a relatively heavy bomb load, it could not carry bombs any bigger than 907kg (2000lb) – the largest size when the design was completed in 1938. Operations began with daylight attacks in February 1941, soon switched to night, and by 1943 the Stirling was used mainly as a glider tug, transport and carrier of ECM jamming and spoofing devices for 100 Group.

The 2374 aircraft produced included 756 Mk I bombers with 1189kW (1595hp) Hercules XI engines, 875 Mk III bombers with a revised dorsal turret, 579 Mk IV paratroop and glider-towing aircraft without nose and dorsal turrets, and 160 Mk V unarmed transports.

SPECIFICATIONS

SHORT STIRLING

Manufacturer: **Short Bros., Ltd.**	Crew: **7/8**
Type: **Heavy Bomber**	Powerplant: **4 x Bristol Hercules XVI**
Length: **26.59m (87ft 3in)**	Armament: **7 x 0.303in MG**
Span: **30.20m (99ft 1in)**	Bomb load: **6350kg (14,000lb)**
Height: **6.93m (22ft 9in)**	First flight: **14 May 1939**
Maximum speed: **434km/h (270mph)**	Initial climb: **244m (800ft) per min**
Service ceiling: **Not Given**	Weight (empty): **21,274kg (46,900lb)**
Range: **3235km (2010 miles)**	Weight (loaded): **31,752kg (70,000lb)**

SHORT SUNDERLAND

SPECIFICATIONS

SHORT SUNDERLAND

Manufacturer: **Short Bros., Ltd.**	Crew: **10**
Type: **Maritime Recon'**	Powerplant: **4 x Bristol Pegasus XXII**
Length: **26.00m (85ft 3.5in)**	Armament: **8 x 0.303in MG**
Span: **34.38m (112ft 9.5in)**	Bomb load: **907kg (2000lb)**
Height: **10.52m (34ft 6in)**	First flight: **16 October 1937**
Maximum speed: **336km/h (209mph)**	Initial climb: **220m (720ft) per min**
Service ceiling: **4570m (15,000ft)**	Weight (empty): **13,875kg (30,589lb)**
Range: **4023km (2500 miles)**	Weight (loaded): **22,226kg (49,000lb)**

Short had over two decades experience in seaplane and flying boat building when it undertook to design and develop a military, general reconnaissance flying boat for the Air Ministry, which the company derived from S.23 "Empire" class boats. An order for 21 production examples of the S.25 was placed in March 1936, some 18 months before the prototype made its maiden flight in October 1937. The initial production model was the Sunderland Mk I that entered service in summer 1938; by the time war had broken out, four British-based squadrons had converted onto the type. Sunderland Mk I production totalled 90, powered by 753kW (1010hp) Bristol Pegasus engines.

The Sunderland Mk II had more powerful (783kW/1050hp) Bristol Pegasus XVIII radial engines and, later in the production run, a twin-gun dorsal turret in place of the single port and starboard waist-mounted weapons, and the addition of air-to-surface search radar. First flown in June 1942, the Sunderland Mk III was the first major production model of the family and was in essence a late-production Sunderland Mk II with a revised planing hull. The last production model was the Sunderland GR.Mk V, of which 143 were completed up to June 1946 with a significantly improved powerplant, better armament and detail modifications.

SUPERMARINE SEAFIRE

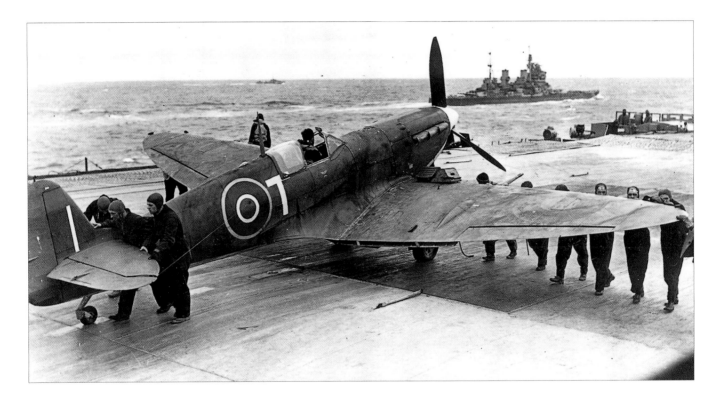

In 1940 the Royal Navy had no better carrier-borne fighter aircraft than the Blackburn Skua, and even with the expected service entry of its Fairey Fulmar replacement the service was faced with the technical and tactical obsolescence of its carrier-borne fighter force. In response, the RN ordered the Seafire, a navalized version of the Spitfire with arrestor gear and catapult spools, for service from June 1942.

The main variants were the Seafire Mk IB (166 conversions from Spitfire Mk VB standard), Seafire Mk IIC (372 aircraft equipped with cannon armament and bombs racks for low- and medium-altitude operations as well as reconnaissance-fighter operations), and the definitive Seafire Mk III (1220 aircraft in the same variants as the Seafire Mk II but with folding wings). There were also 30 Seafire Mk III (Hybrid) aircraft with fixed wings, these later being reclassified as Seafire Mk IIC machines, and the Seafire Mks XV, XVII, 45, 46 and 47 which were post-war developments.

The Seafire offered good performance, but was hampered for carrier-borne operations by its long nose and narrow-track main landing gear units. There were numerous post-war developments of the aircraft, the last of which was finally retired from service with the Royal Navy Volunteer Reserve (RNVR) in 1967.

SPECIFICATIONS

SUPERMARINE SEAFIRE

Manufacturer: **Supermarine Aviation**	Crew: **One**
Type: **Carrier-Borne Fighter**	Powerplant: **1 x RR Merlin 55M**
Length: **9.21m (30ft 2.5in)**	Armament: **2 x cannon, 4 x MG**
Span: **11.23m (36ft 10in)**	Bomb load: **227kg (500lb)**
Height: **3.42m (11ft 2.5in)**	First flight: **Not Given**
Maximum speed: **560km/h (348mph)**	Initial climb: **762m (2501ft) per min**
Service ceiling: **7315m (24,000ft)**	Weight (empty): **2814kg (6204lb)**
Range: **890km (553 miles)**	Weight (loaded): **3465kg (7640lb)**

SUPERMARINE SPITFIRE Mk I

SPECIFICATIONS

SUPERMARINE SPITFIRE Mk I

Manufacturer: **Supermarine Aviation**	Crew: **One**
Type: **Fighter, Fighter-Bomber**	Powerplant: **1 x RR Merlin 45**
Length: **9.12m (29ft 11in)**	Armament: **8 x 0.303in MG**
Span: **11.23m (36ft 10in)**	Bomb load: **227kg (500lb)**
Height: **3.02m (9ft 11in)**	First flight: **5 March 1936**
Maximum speed: **594km/h (394mph)**	Initial climb: **1204m (3950ft) per min**
Service ceiling: **11,125m (36,500ft)**	Weight (empty): **2267kg (4998lb)**
Range: **1827km (1,135 miles)**	Weight (loaded): **2911kg (6417lb)**

When he began designing the Spitfire in the mid-1930s, R.J. Mitchell could hardly have known that he was creating one of the most famous of all aircraft. Mitchell brought to the project valuable experience gained through the Schneider Trophy races, and fortunately had a virtually free rein when creating the Spitfire. The aircraft, known initially as the Type 300, was developed around the Rolls-Royce PV 12 (later Merlin) engine, and the prototype was subsequently ordered into production in June 1936 as the Spitfire Mk I. Service deliveries of 310 Mk I aircraft began in July 1938 and at the outbreak of war the RAF had some 18 squadrons of them.

The Spitfire's reputation was cemented during the Battle of Britain, and although less numerous than the Hurricane it proved a better match for the Bf 109E owing to its exceptional manoeuvrability. The Mk I was followed by 1566 IBs with twin 20mm cannon, the Mk IIA and IIB with Merlin XII, the one-off experimental Mk III with Merlin XX, the Mk IV, 229 photo-reconnaissance versions of the Spitfire Mk V, and then by the Mk V with strengthened fuselage for Merlin 45 or Merlin 50 engines, drop tanks and bomb provision. Suffix LF designated an aircraft with the low-altitude clipped wing and F the standard wing. A, B and C were all different armament fits.

SUPERMARINE SPITFIRE PR Mk XI

When introduced into service in early 1941 the Focke Wulf Fw 190 immediately proved itself superior to any British fighter and Supermarine urgently sought ways of improving the performance of the Spitfire to counter it. In June 1942 the Mk XI entered service, supposedly as an "interim" measure before other more capable versions became available, but in the event it proved one of the most successful of all Spitfire variants. The Mk XI was in effect really just the airframe of the Spitfire Mk VC (Spitfire Mk V with two cannon and two machine-guns and provision for carrying bombs) with the uprated Merlin 60 series of engines. Production totalled 5665 aircraft in low-, medium- and high-altitude sub-variants; the Spitfire LF.Mk XVI (1054 aircraft) was a development with the 1178kW (1580hp) Packard Merlin 266.

There were also photo-reconnaissance versions such as the Spitfire PR.Mks IX, X and XI, succeeding earlier Spitfire photo-reconnaissance adaptations: the PR.Mk IX was converted from the Mk IX fighter, but the 16 and 471 PR.Mks X and XI were new-build aircraft with Merlin 61, 63 or 70 engines. The 16 PR Mk Xs had a pressurized cockpit and increased fuel tankage; the PR XI was essentially the same but was unpressurized and was the mainstay of the RAF PR units from 1943 to 1945.

SPECIFICATIONS

SUPERMARINE SPITFIRE PR Mk XI

Manufacturer: **Supermarine Aviation**	Crew: **One**
Type: **Fighter, Fighter-Bomber**	Powerplant: **1 x RR Merlin 61**
Length: **9.46m (31ft)**	Armament: **2 x cannon, 4 x MG**
Span: **11.23m (36ft 10in)**	Bomb load: **454kg (1000lb)**
Height: **3.85m (12ft 7.75in)**	First flight: **1942**
Maximum speed: **655km/h (408mph)**	Initial climb: **1204m (3950ft) per min**
Service ceiling: **12,105m (43,000ft)**	Weight (empty): **2545kg (5610lb)**
Range: **1576km (980 miles)**	Weight (loaded): **4309kg (9500lb)**

SUPERMARINE WALRUS

SPECIFICATIONS

SUPERMARINE WALRUS

Manufacturer:
Supermarine Aviation

Crew:
Four

Type:
Spotter Amphibian

Powerplant:
1 x Bristol Pegasus VI

Length:
11.35m (37ft 3in)

Armament:
3 x 0.303in MG

Span:
13.97m (45ft 10in)

Bomb load:
272kg (600lb)

Height:
4.65m (15ft 3in)

First flight:
Not Given

Maximum speed:
217km/h (135mph)

Initial climb:
Not Available

Service ceiling:
5210m (17,100ft)

Weight (empty):
2223kg (4900lb)

Range:
966km (600 miles)

Weight (loaded):
3266kg (7200lb)

The Walrus was evolved from the Supermarine Seal, a three-man deck-landing amphibian aircraft ordered by the Royal Air Force for use as a fleet spotter to operate from Royal Navy aircraft carriers. A converted Seal II became the prototype Seagull, a folding-wing biplane with retractable landing gear that came into service in the early 1920s.

The prototype Mk V version of the Seagull was fitted with a Bristol Pegasus engine in a pusher configuration and was stressed for catapult-launching. After evaluation by the Fleet Air Arm this version was adopted under the name Walrus Mk I as standard equipment for the Royal Navy's catapult-equipped ships. Production began in 1936 of an eventual 746 "boats", this total including 191 Walrus Mk IIs with a Saro wooden hull and Bristol Pegasus VI engine.

The Walrus saw extensive service in World War II, flying with the Australian, British and New Zealand navies. Known universally as the "Shagbat", the Supermarine Walrus was also used in the air-sea rescue role, ensuring it a place in the hearts of many aircrew. It was superseded in service from 1944 by the Sea Otter, which was essentially a Walrus airframe with a tractor engine, and the last biplane to enter service with the Fleet Air Arm.

VICKERS WELLESLEY

Vickers built a large biplane to meet the RAF's G.4/31 Specification that called for a general-purpose and torpedo bomber, but it was so uninspiring that the company decided to build at its own risk a monoplane using the radical and innovative geodetic structure pioneered by Dr Barnes Wallis on the company's airships. The Wellesley emerged for its first flight in June 1935 as a fabric-covered cantilever monoplane with a wing of high aspect ratio and it proved so dramatically superior that the Air Ministry lost its fear of monoplanes and ordered 96 Wellesley Mk I aircraft, optimized for the medium-bomber role with the bombs carried in two underwing panniers. The Mk I entered service in April 1937, and production up to May 1938 totalled 176 aircraft, most of the later aircraft being completed (unofficially designated Mk II) with a continuous "glasshouse" canopy bridging the front and rear cockpits. The aircraft was distinguished by the very long-span wing, extreme cruise efficiency and a reliable engine, prompting the establishment of the Long Range Development Flight that made a number of record-breaking flights, one of them a 48-hour non-stop trip from Ismalia, Egypt, to Darwin, Australia – a distance of some 11,525km (7162 miles). The Wellesley saw useful service during the first part of the war until late 1942.

SPECIFICATIONS

VICKERS WELLESLEY

Manufacturer: **Vickers-Armstrong Ltd**	Crew: **Two**
Type: **General-Purpose Bomber**	Powerplant: **1 x Bristol Pegasus XX**
Length: **11.96m (39ft 3in)**	Armament: **2 x 0.303in MG**
Span: **22.73m (74ft 7in)**	Bomb load: **907kg (2000lb)**
Height: **3.75m (12ft 4in)**	First flight: **9 June 1935**
Maximum speed: **369km/h (228mph)**	Initial climb: **366m (1200ft) per min**
Service ceiling: **10,060m (33,000ft)**	Weight (empty): **2889kg (6369lb)**
Range: **1786km (1110 miles)**	Weight (loaded): **5035kg (11,100lb)**

VICKERS WELLINGTON

SPECIFICATIONS

VICKERS WELLINGTON

Manufacturer: Vickers-Armstrong Ltd.	**Crew:** Six
Type: Medium Bomber	**Powerplant:** 2 x Bristol Hercules
Length: 19.68m (64ft 7in)	**Armament:** 7 x 0.303in MG
Span: 26.26m (86ft 2in)	**Bomb load:** 2041kg (4500lb)
Height: 5.31m (17ft 5in)	**First flight:** 15 June 1936
Maximum speed: 410km/h (255mph)	**Initial climb:** 320m (1050ft) per min
Service ceiling: 6705m (22,000ft)	**Weight (empty):** 10,194kg (22,474lb)
Range: 3033km (1885 miles)	**Weight (loaded):** 16,556kg (36,500lb)

The geodetic construction successfully employed on the Wellesley was used again on the Wellington, which bore the brunt of the bomber effort in the early stages of the war until large numbers of four-engined heavy bombers became available. There were some difficulties in applying it to wings, cut-out nacelles and fuselages with large bomb doors but the prototype demonstrated good performance and the type was put into service in October 1938. The initial model was the Wellington Mk I with 746kW (1000hp) Pegasus XVIII radial engines. Development as a bomber continued via the Mk III with Rolls-Royce Merlin Vee engines, Mk III with Hercules III or XI radial engines, Mk IV with Pratt & Whitney Twin Wasp radial engines, Mk VI with Merlin engines, and Mk X with Hercules engines.

As the Wellington became obsolescent in the bomber role it found increasing employment as a maritime type for Coastal Command. The specialized variant was the Wellington GR.Mk VIII, a development of the Mk IC bomber with either ASV.Mk II radar or a Leigh Light for anti-ship and anti-submarine operations, and which entered service in spring 1942. The following GR.Mks XI, XII, XIII and XIV had different engine and radar fits for anti-shipping anti-submarine, mine clearance and transport work.

WESTLAND LYSANDER

Resulting from a 1934 requirement for a battlefield reconnaissance and army cooperation aircraft, the distinctive Lysander was designed to provide its two-man crew with the best possible fields of vision to the front and sides, especially towards the ground, and was therefore planned as a high-wing cabin monoplane with a substantial fuselage carrying a large glazed cockpit. The prototype first flew in June 1936, and when it entered service in June 1938 it was used for artillery spotting and message pick-ups. However, in wartime the Lysander blossomed into a remarkable multi-role aircraft. The first He 111 to be shot down in BEF territory fell to the modestly armed Lysander, and during the battle for France it was operated as a night-fighter and ground-attack aircraft, also making precision supply drops over Calais. Production versions were the Lysander Mk I (169), Lysander Mk II (517) with the 675kW (905hp) Bristol Perseus XII engine, Lysander Mk III (517) with the Mercury XX engine, and Mk IIIA (347) – an improved version of the Mk III. From 1941 it was increasingly used as a target-tug (100 new TT.Mk IIIA aircraft with 70 conversions) and to deliver agents into Europe; the best known variant was probably the IIISCW, used for agent-insertion or -recovery, which had a belly tank and ladder to provide access to the lofty cockpit.

SPECIFICATIONS

WESTLAND LYSANDER

Manufacturer: **Westland Aircraft Ltd.**	Crew: **1/2**
Type: **Tactical Reconnaissance**	Powerplant: **1 x Bristol Mercury XII**
Length: **9.30m (30ft 6in)**	Armament: **3 x 0.303in MG**
Span: **15.24m (50ft)**	Bomb load: **227kg (500lb)**
Height: **3.35m (11ft)**	First flight: **15 June 1936**
Maximum speed: **369km/h (229mph)**	Initial climb: **580m (1900ft) per min**
Service ceiling: **7925m (26,000ft)**	Weight (empty): **1844kg (4065lb)**
Range: **966km (600 miles)**	Weight (loaded): **3402kg (7500lb)**

BREDA Ba 65

SPECIFICATIONS

BREDA Ba 65

Manufacturer:
Societa Ernesto Breda

Crew:
One

Type:
Ground-Attack

Powerplant:
1 x Fiat A.80 RC.41

Length:
9.30m (30ft 6.25in)

Armament:
4 x MG

Span:
12.10m (39ft 8.5in)

Bomb load:
500kg (1102lb)

Height:
3.20m (10ft 6in)

First flight:
September 1935

Maximum speed:
430km/h (267mph)

Initial climb:
Not Available

Service ceiling:
6300m (20,670ft)

Weight (empty):
2400kg (5291lb)

Range:
550km (342 miles)

Weight (loaded):
2950kg (6504lb)

Breda began building aircraft in 1917 and soon grew into one of the largest Italian aeronautical concerns. The Ba 65 was schemed as a multi-role warplane capable of fulfilling the roles of interceptor, light bomber or reconnaissance/attack aircraft. The prototype flew in September 1935 in the form of a low-wing monoplane of all-metal construction (except for the fabric-covered trailing edges). The Regia Aeronautica ordered 81 of the aircraft equipped with the French Gnome-Rhône radial engine that had been fitted to the prototype. An initial batch of 13 single-seat aircraft were sent for evaluation in Spain with the Aviazione Legionare; operational experience there revealed that the Ba 65 was only suitable for the attack role and it was thereafter seconded to the assault wings (stormi).

A second batch of 137 aircraft was delivered between 1938 and July 1939, this total included some that were fitted with an open observer's station above the trailing edge of the rear wing, and a small number fitted with a Breda L turret. Both had a single 7.7mm machine-gun in this position. During the early days of the war over the North African desert, Ba 65s were pitched against the British Royal Air Force, but suffered from appalling reliability problems and by February 1941 no serviceable examples remained.

CAPRONI Ca 133

As Mussolini's Italy began to expand by restoring the "lost colonies" and forcibly building up an overseas empire, a need arose for an aircraft suitable for operations in these new territories; one in the mould of the British Vickers Vincent and Westland Wapiti. The Societa Italiana Caproni produced the Ca 101 to meet this need, with at least 200 being delivered in the early 1930s to serve as bomber, troop-carrier, reconnaissance, ground-attack and supply aircraft. This was followed by the Ca 111, with an uprated powerplant, which served in Ethiopia and Albania – and in 1935 by the Ca 133 which introduced a number of drag-lowering features, namely neat long-chord cowlings (housing three uprated engines), together with faired legs and spatted wheels for the main landing gear units, an improved tail unit and split flaps on the wing trailing edges. The Italian air force soon realized that despite its improvements the type was suitable only for colonial use in North and East Africa. At the outbreak of war it equipped 14 Squadriglie di Bombardimento in these theatres. Ca 133 production totalled 419 aircraft, and conversions included 21 Ca 133S air ambulances and 329 Ca 133T transports with reduced armament. The Ca 133 suffered heavy losses at the hands of British fighters, although some found their way to the Russian Front after Italy's capitulation in 1943.

SPECIFICATIONS

CAPRONI Ca 133

Manufacturer: **Societa Italiana Caproni**	Crew: **Three**
Type: **Bomber and Transport**	Powerplant: **3 x Piaggio Stella PVII**
Length: **15.36m (50ft 4.75in)**	Armament: **4 x 7.7mm MG**
Span: **21.24m (68ft 8in)**	Bomb load: **1200kg (2646lb)**
Height: **4.00m (13ft 1in)**	First flight: **1935**
Maximum speed: **265km/h (165mph)**	Initial climb: **Not Available**
Service ceiling: **5500m (18,045ft)**	Weight (empty): **4190kg (9237lb)**
Range: **1350km (838 miles)**	Weight (loaded): **6700kg (14,771lb)**

MACCHI 202 FOLGORE

SPECIFICATIONS

MACCHI 202 FOLGORE

Manufacturer: **Aeronautica Macchi**	Crew: **One**
Type: **Interceptor Fighter**	Powerplant: **1 x Alfa Romeo RC 41-1**
Length: **8.85m (29ft 0.5in)**	Armament: **2 x 12.7mm MG**
Span: **10.58m (34ft 8.5in)**	Bomb load: **None**
Height: **3.04m (9ft 11.5in)**	First flight: **10 August 1940**
Maximum speed: **595km/h (370mph)**	Initial climb: **Not Available**
Service ceiling: **11,500m (37,730ft)**	Weight (empty): **2350kg (5181lb)**
Range: **765km (475 miles)**	Weight (loaded): **3010kg (6636lb)**

The finest Italian fighters of World War II all came from a team led by Mario Castoldi at Macchi of Varese. The company had gained great experience from their involvement in the Schneider Trophy races, yet their first low-wing fighter, the MC.200, was both underpowered and underarmed. Castoldi remained confident in the basic design, but was convinced that its full potential could only be realized with more engine power. Daimler-Benz DB 601A engines were sourced from Germany and fitted to the aircraft to produce the MC.202 Folgore prototype, which first flew in August 1940. Rushed into production, the MC.202 had a new fuselage for the imported engine and a larger cockpit.

Alfa Romeo subsequently acquired a licence to build the powerplant, but the limited availability of this meant that production was slow and totalled only some 1500 aircraft. A further improved version of the same airframe was the MC.205V Veltro, which first flew in April 1942 with a licence-built version of the DB 605 engine and began operations in July 1943. Later machines had 20mm cannon rather than 7.7mm machine-guns in the wings, and most of the 265-odd aircraft served with Aeronautica Nazionale Republicana after Italy's 1943 armistice with the Allies. A high-altitude version existed only in prototype – the MC.205N Orione.

SAVOIA-MARCHETTI SM 79 SPARVIERO

Often derided by uninformed observers, the SM 79 was a fine and robust bomber that unfailingly operated in difficult conditions and is recognized as one of the finest torpedo bombers of World War II. The *Sparviero* (Sparrowhawk) was first flown in 1934 as the SM.79P civil transport prototype with accommodation for eight-passengers. Painted in both civil and military liveries and fitted with various engines, the prototype set numerous world records in 1935–36. Subsequently it was developed as a medium reconnaissance bomber with an uprated powerplant of three Alfa Romeo 126 radial engines and a large ventral gondola.

Production examples of this SM.79-I entered service in late 1936, and established an excellent reputation with the Aviacon Legionaria in Spain. However, the SM 79 was most successfully employed in the role of torpedo bomber, the first dedicated variant being the SM.79-II (two 450mm torpedoes and a powerplant of three 746kW/1000hp Piaggio P.XI RC.40 or 768kW/1030hp Fiat A.80 RC.41 radial engines). The final Italian model was the SM.79-II, an improved SM.79-II with heavier defensive armament but no ventral gondola. Deliveries to the Regia Aeronautica totalled 1230 aircraft, and about 100 others were exported in a number of twin-engined forms.

SPECIFICATIONS

SAVOIA-MARCHETTI SM 79 SPARVIERO

Manufacturer: **Savoia Marchetti**	*Crew:* **4/5**
Type: **Medium Recon' Bomber**	*Powerplant:* **3 x Alfa Romeo RC.34**
Length: **15.62m (51ft 3.1in)**	*Armament:* **4 x MG**
Span: **21.20m (69ft 2.7in)**	*Bomb load:* **2756lb (1250kg)**
Height: **4.40m (14ft 5.25in)**	*First flight:* **Late 1934**
Maximum speed: **430km/h (267mph)**	*Initial climb:* **253m (830ft) per min**
Service ceiling: **6500m (21,325ft)**	*Weight (empty):* **6800kg (14,991lb)**
Range: **1900km (1181 miles)**	*Weight (loaded):* **10,480kg (23,104lb)**

KAWANISHI E7K "ALF"

SPECIFICATIONS

KAWANISHI E7K2 "ALF"

Manufacturer: **Kawanishi**	Crew: **Three**
Type: **Recon' Floatplane**	Powerplant: **1 x Mitsubishi Zuisei 11**
Length: **10.50m (34ft 5.5in)**	Armament: **3 x MG**
Span: **14m (45ft 11.25in)**	Bomb load: **120kg (265lb)**
Height: **4.85m (15ft 10.5in)**	First flight: **August 1938**
Maximum speed: **275km/h (171mph)**	Initial climb: **Not Available**
Service ceiling: **7060m (23,165ft)**	Weight (empty): **2100kg (4630lb)**
Range: **not available**	Weight (loaded): **3300kg (7275lb)**

In 1932 the Imperial Japanese Navy contracted Kawanishi Kokuki Kabushiki Kaisha for a prototype of its E7K1, the proposed replacement for the E5K then in service. The newer aircraft was a three-seat biplane of unequal span powered by a 462kW (620hp) engine and which was first flown in February 1933. The prototype was handed over to the navy's aircraft evaluation unit in May and flown in a series of competitive service trials against the Aichi B-6.

The Kawanishi type was subsequently ordered into production in May 1934 and the first examples rolled out of the factory early the next year. In service it proved popular on account of its stable and predictable handling characteristics, although the aircraft was somewhat let down by the unreliability of the Hiro engine. Substituting the -91 version of the engine in later aircraft did not cure the problem and for the following E7K2 the manufacturer adopted a Mitsubishi Zuisei 11 radial piston engine (649kW/870hp).

First flown in this form in August 1938, the E7K2 was adopted and entered service in early 1939. By the time that war had broken out in the Pacific in December 1941, most of the 183 E7K1 produced had been relegated to training duties, although the 350 E7K2 aircraft were active until 1943.

KAWASAKI Ki 61 "TONY"

Kawasaki Kokuyu Kogyo Kabushiki Kaisha purchased a licence to produce the German DB 601 in 1937 and revised and lightened it to produce the Ha-40. The Ki-60 low-wing monoplane fighter was planned around this, but proved disappointing and work focused on a lighter fighter identified as the Ki-61 *Hien* (Swallow), unique among Japan's first-line warplanes in being powered by an inverted-Vee piston engine. The first of 12 prototype and pre-production aircraft flew in December 1941, and revealed good performance and handling, reaching a top speed of some 592km/h (368mph). The prototype was tested extensively during the following spring against captured examples of the P-40E and a Bf 109 sent from Germany, along with 800 Mauser MG 151 cannon that were fitted to early production aircraft despite the unreliability of the supply of the electrically fused ammunition. The Ki-61-I entered service in February 1943 and first saw combat in New Guinea in April 1943. Some 1380 aircraft were delivered in two sub-variants differentiated by their armament, followed by 1274 Ki-61 Kai fighters with a lengthened fuselage and different armament. Further development resulted in the Ki-61-II Kai, optimized for high-altitude operations with the unreliable Kawasaki Ha-140 engine, in two sub-variants again distinguishable by armament fit.

SPECIFICATIONS

KAWASAKI Ki 61 "TONY"

Manufacturer: **Kawasaki**	*Crew:* **One**
Type: **(Ki-61-Ib) Fighter**	*Powerplant:* **1 x Kawasaki Ha-40**
Length: **8.75m (28ft 8.5in)**	*Armament:* **4 x 12.7mm MG**
Span: **12.10m (39ft 4.25in)**	*Bomb load:* **None**
Height: **3.70m (12ft 1.75in)**	*First flight:* **December 1941**
Maximum speed: **592km/h (368mph)**	*Initial climb:* **675m (2200ft) per min**
Service ceiling: **11,600m (37,730ft)**	*Weight (empty):* **2210kg (4872lb)**
Range: **1100km (684 miles)**	*Weight (loaded):* **3250kg (7165lb)**

MITSUBISHI A6M ZERO-SEN

SPECIFICATIONS

MITSUBISHI A6M ZERO-SEN

Manufacturer:
Mitsubishi

Crew:
One

Type:
Fighter, Fighter-Bomber

Powerplant:
1 x Nakajima NK1C

Length:
9.06m (29ft 8.75in)

Armament:
2 x cannon, 2 x MG

Span:
12.00m (39ft 4.5in)

Bomb load:
120kg (265lb)

Height:
3.05m (10ft)

First flight:
1 April 1939

Maximum speed:
534km/h (332mph)

Initial climb:
1370m (4500ft) per min

Service ceiling:
10,000m (32,810ft)

Weight (empty):
1680kg (3704lb)

Range:
3104km (1929 miles)

Weight (loaded):
2796kg (6164lb)

This most famous of all Japanese combat aircraft was developed to a tough 1937 Imperial Japanese Navy requirement, and although it entered service in summer 1940 and was used in the Manchurian campaign neither British nor American staff appear to have been aware of it (this despite the reports of the Flying Tigers volunteer force). The aircraft provided a rude shock at Pearl Harbor and Singapore, for it possessed performance equal and greater to any land-based fighter in the Pacific theatre – at that time a remarkable achievement for a carrier-based fighter. When fitted with a centreline drop tank the Zero had phenomenal range, afforded by sophisticated engine/propeller management techniques.

The A6M was generally known in the West as the Zero, a name derived from its Japanese name *Reisen* (meaning "zero fighter") that resulted from its adoption in the Japanese year 2600 (1940). Lack of a successor meant that the Zero was maintained in development and production (11,280 aircraft) past its effective limits. The type reached its apogee as a dogfighter in the A6M2, while the A6M3 had greater power but shorter range, the A6M5 heavier firepower and the A6M6 better protection and greater fighter-bomber capability. After the Battle of Midway the A6M found itself increasingly outclassed and most ended up as kamikaze aircraft.

MITSUBISHI G4M "BETTY"

The G4M was the Imperial Japanese Navy air force's premier heavy bomber in World War II, yet the insistence in the 1938 specification to which it was built that the aircraft should have a range of 3700km (2000 miles) with a full bomb load meant that reducing its weight took priority over defence and the aircraft was subsequently highly vulnerable (and thus unpopular). Armour plating, self-sealing fuel tanks and a sturdy structure able to absorb battle damage were all sacrificed in the drive to attain acceptable range. The first of two G4M1 prototypes flew in October 1939, and the type entered service early in 1941. Production totalled 1200 G4M1 aircraft in variants such as the Convoy Fighter Escort (five 20mm trainable cannon), Model 11 Attack Bomber and Model 12 Attack Bomber, the last with MK4E engines. Trainer and transport variants were then created as conversions. The G4M2 entered service from mid-1943 with an uprated powerplant, a laminar-flow wing, a larger tailplane, additional fuel capacity and heavier defensive armament for better overall capability, but only at the cost of reduced agility. Recognition of the vulnerability of the aircraft brought the G4M3 with armoured crew areas and a wing revised with self-sealing tanks, but too late to be of any real use. Only 60 had been completed before Japan's surrender in 1945.

SPECIFICATIONS

MITSUBISHI G4M

Manufacturer: **Mitsubishi**	Crew: **Seven**
Type: **Medium Bomber**	Powerplant: **2 x Mitsubishi MK4A**
Length: **20.00m (65ft 7.25in)**	Armament: **1 x cannon, 2 x MG**
Span: **25.00m (82ft 0.25in)**	Bomb load: **800kg (1764lb)**
Height: **6.00m (19ft 8.25in)**	First flight: **October 1939**
Maximum speed: **428km/h (266mph)**	Initial climb: **550m (1800ft) per min**
Service ceiling: **Not Available**	Weight (empty): **6800kg (14,991lb)**
Range: **6033km (3749 miles)**	Weight (loaded): **9500kg (20,944lb)**

BOEING B-17 FLYING FORTRESS

SPECIFICATIONS

BOEING B-17 FLYING FORTRESS

Manufacturer: **Boeing Aircraft Company**	Crew: **10**
Type: **(B-17G) Heavy Bomber**	Powerplant: **4 x Wright R-1820-97**
Length: **22.78m (74ft 9 in)**	Armament: **12 x 0.50in MG**
Span: **31.63m (103ft 9.4in)**	Bomb load: **7983kg (17,600lb)**
Height: **5.82m (19ft 1in)**	First flight: **28 July 1935**
Maximum speed: **486km/h (302mph)**	Initial climb: **164m (540ft) per min**
Service ceiling: **10,850m (35,600ft)**	Weight (empty): **44,560lb (20,212kg)**
Range: **2897km (1800 miles)**	Weight (loaded): **72,000lb (32,659kg)**

In May 1934 the US Army Air Corps (USAAC) issued a specification for a multi-engined anti-shipping bomber. In response, Boeing built the Model 299 as a private-venture prototype with provision for a 2177kg (4800lb) bomb load, which was later evaluated as the XB-17. The USAAC was expected to select the twin-engined Martin B-10, but in the event orders were placed for 14 YB-17 and YB-17A service test aircraft later accepted into service as the B-17 and B-17A aircraft. These models were followed by the slightly modified B-17B (nose), B-17C (defensive armament) and B-17D (extra crew member). Some 20 B-17Cs were transferred to the UK as Fortress Mk I machines; most of the B-17D bombers were stationed in the Far East, where about half were destroyed by Japan on 7 December 1941. The first large-scale production model was the B-17E, with a new tail unit for improved, high-altitude stability, and revised defensive armament including a twin-gun tail position and power-operated twin-gun dorsal and ventral turrets. Most widely produced was the B-17F, which introduced a frameless Plexiglas nose and structural strengthening. The final bomber model was the B-17G Flying Fortress, with a power-operated chin turret. Deliveries of 8680 aircraft began in September 1943, these undertaking the weight of the US bomber effort in Europe from 1944.

BOEING B-29 SUPERFORTRESS

The design and development of the Model 345, the B-29, was a huge undertaking. The process began in March 1938 when Boeing submitted a study for a new bomber with pressurized cabin and tricycle landing gear. This evolved into the Model 345 and after 14 months of intensive development and testing of two prototypes an order was placed for 14 YB-29s and 500 production aircraft. The production effort for these aircraft involved Boeing, Bell, North American and General Motors and later Martin. The B-29 was hugely complex and represented a leap forward in terms of engine power, gross weight, wing loading, pressurization, armament, airborne systems and basic structure. Entering service in June 1944, by VJ Day some 3000 aircraft had been built. These were predominantly stationed in the Marianas Islands and used in a campaign of massed high level bombing to neutralize the war-making potential of Japan by burning her cities and crippling her industries. When this failed to force the Japanese to surrender, a B-29 was equipped to drop the atomic weapons that destroyed Hiroshima and Nagasaki on 6 and 9 August 1945. The baseline B-29 (2458 built) was complemented by the B-29A (1119) with a greater span and improved forward dorsal barbette, and the B-29B (310) with reduced defensive armament but a greater bomb load and speed.

SPECIFICATIONS

BOEING B-29 SUPERFORTRESS

Manufacturer: **Boeing Aircraft Company**	Crew: **Nine**
Type: **Long-Range H'vy Bomber**	Powerplant: **4 x Wright R-3350-23**
Length: **30.18m (99ft)**	Armament: **1 x cannon, 8 x MG**
Span: **43.05m (141ft 2.75in)**	Bomb load: **9072kg (20,000lb)**
Height: **9.02m (29ft 7in)**	First flight: **21 September 1942**
Maximum speed: **576km/h (358mph)**	Initial climb: **160m (526ft) per min**
Service ceiling: **9710m (31,850ft)**	Weight (empty): **31,816kg (70,140lb)**
Range: **5830 miles (9382km)**	Weight (loaded): **56,246kg (124,000lb)**

BREWSTER F2S BUFFALO

SPECIFICATIONS

BREWSTER F2S BUFFALO

Manufacturer:
Brewster Aeronautical

Crew:
One

Type:
Fighter, Fighter-Bomber

Powerplant:
1 x Wright R-1820-40

Length:
8.03m (26ft 4in)

Armament:
4 x 0.50in MG

Span:
10.67m (35ft)

Bomb load:
105kg (232lb)

Height:
3.68m (12ft 1in)

First flight:
January 1938

Maximum speed:
517km/h (321mph)

Initial climb:
698m (2290ft) per min

Service ceiling:
10,120m (33,200ft)

Weight (empty):
2146kg (4732lb)

Range:
2704km (1680 miles)

Weight (loaded):
3247kg (7159lb)

The dumpy little Buffalo was one of the first aircraft built by the Brewster Company, which in 1935 secured an order for a US Navy scout-bomber. It also entered a competition for a carrier-based monoplane fighter and won. With such a lack of experience in aircraft design and production, it is not surprising that the first XF2A-1 prototype took almost two years to build. This first flew in January 1938 and in June of that year the Brewster machine was, perhaps surprisingly, selected in preference to the Grumman G.36 Wildcat. Of the 54 F2A-1 production aircraft ordered only 11 entered service on USS *Saratoga* in July 1939 with the 701kW (940hp) R-1820-34 engine (the balance were supplied to Finland).

The US Navy took 43 and 108 examples of the F2A-2 and F2A-3, the former with an uprated engine and armament and the latter with self-sealing tanks and a longer nose. The F2A was generally unsuccessful in American service, but it was also operated by Finland, which was the only country to use the type with major success, Belgium, of which 38 were delivered to the UK as Buffalo Mk Is, the Dutch East Indies, the UK as Buffalo Mk Is, and Australia. In the Pacific the Buffalo fought valiantly against the Japanese, but was outclassed as well as outnumbered and suffered accordingly.

CONSOLIDATED B-24 LIBERATOR

Although conceived some five years after the B-17, the B-24 represented no great improvement over the older aircraft. In fact it was something of a handful for inexperienced pilots, and was also the most complex and expensive combat aircraft built thus far. Yet it was produced in larger numbers (18,431 machines) than any other US warplane of World War II and served on every wartime front and with every Allied nation.

The slightly curious layout was dictated by the need to place the slender wing above the tall fuselage bomb bay. This wing was efficient in cruising flight, which, combined with great fuel capacity, gave the Liberator a longer range than any contemporary landplane. First flown in XB-24 prototype form in December 1939, the first major production models were the B-24D (2738 aircraft), the generally similar B-24E (791 aircraft) and the B-24G (430 aircraft with a power-operated nose turret).

The B-24 made its operational debut in June 1942 with the long-range raids mounted from Egypt against the Ploesti oilfields in Romania. There were other developments, too numerous to list here, which allowed the aircraft to operate on long-range maritime reconnaissance and transport duties, a photo-reconnaissance platform and as a fuel tanker.

SPECIFICATIONS

CONSOLIDATED B-24 LIBERATOR

Manufacturer: **Consolidated Vultee**	Crew: **10**
Type: **Long-Range H'vy Bomber**	Powerplant: **4 x P & W R-1830-43**
Length: **20.22m (66ft 4in)**	Armament: **9 x 0.50in MG**
Span: **33.53m (110ft)**	Bomb load: **3992kg (8800lb)**
Height: **4.46m (17ft 11in)**	First flight: **29 December 1939**
Maximum speed: **488km/h (303mph)**	Initial climb: **274m (900ft) per min**
Service ceiling: **9755m (32,000ft)**	Weight (empty): **14,490kg (32,605lb)**
Range: **4586km (2850 miles)**	Weight (loaded): **27,216kg (60,000lb)**

CONSOLIDATED CATALINA

SPECIFICATIONS

CONSOLIDATED CATALINA

Manufacturer: **Consolidated Vultee**	Crew: **Nine**
Type: **Maritime Recon'**	Powerplant: **2 x P & W R-1830-92**
Length: **19.45m (63ft 10in)**	Armament: **5 x MG**
Span: **31.70m (104ft)**	Bomb load: **2041kg (4500lb)**
Height: **5.76m (18ft 11in)**	First flight: **21 March 1935**
Maximum speed: **288km/h (179mph)**	Initial climb: **158m (518ft) per min**
Service ceiling: **4480m (14,700ft)**	Weight (empty): **9485kg (20,910lb)**
Range: **5713 km (3550 miles)**	Weight (loaded): **16,067kg (35,420lb)**

Against strong competition from Douglas, Consolidated won a 1933 competition to supply the US Navy with its first cantilever monoplane flying boat. The resulting Consolidated PBY series, now universally known as the Catalina after its British designation, has become a classic, built in larger numbers than all other flying boats combined. The XP3Y-1 prototype made its impressive maiden flight in March 1934 and the US Navy subsequently placed a huge order for 60 PBY-1 aircraft. These were followed by 50 PBY-2s, 66 PBY-3s with uprated engines, 33 PBY-4 with further uprated engines and 1024 PBY-5 with still more power and with waist blisters rather than hatches. In 1938 the USSR bought three and urgently tooled up to build an eventual total of more than 400 of its own version.

Retractable tricycle landing gear was introduced in November 1939 with the production designation PBY-5A, of which 794 were delivered to the US Navy. The Royal Air Force received 225 similar PBY-5Bs. Further variants were the PBY-6A (235 machines) with revised armament and a larger tail, and the Naval Aircraft Factory PBN-1 Nomad (156 machines), to a PBY-5A standard but with a larger tail and increased fuel capacity and armament. The PBY's endurance and stability made it ideal for long-range maritime patrol and anti-submarine work.

CURTISS P-40D (KITTYHAWK MK I)

During 1940 Curtiss redesigned the Model 81 in an attempt to improve its performance. The changes included installation of the Allison V-1710-39 engine, allowing the nose to be shortened and the radiator deepened, thus changing the appearance of the aircraft. Additional armour was added, along with an underfuselage hardpoint, and the fuselage guns were deleted; standard armament thereafter was four 0.50in guns in the wings.

The RAF ordered 560 of the improved version in 1940, and it first flew in May 1941 as the Kittyhawk Mk I. Curtiss identified the aircraft as the Hawk 87-A2 and the USAAC, which had ordered the aircraft in September 1940, called it the P-40D. Only 22 of this version were delivered before production for the USAAF switched to the P-40E (Kittyhawk Mk IA), which had two additional wing guns. The next development, the P-40F (Kittyhawk II), involved installing the Packard V-1650 (Rolls-Royce Merlin) engine into a lengthened P-40D fuselage.

Great Britain also purchased, or received under the Lend-Lease scheme, Kittyhawk Mk II to IV variants of the P-40F, K/M and N, each version heavier and thus less manoeuvrable than its predecessor. Some 2097 of the American aircraft were also shipped to the Soviet Union for service on the Eastern Front.

SPECIFICATIONS

CURTISS P-40D (KITTYHAWK MK I)

Manufacturer: **Curtiss-Wright Corp.**	*Crew:* **One**
Type: **Fighter, Fighter-Bomber**	*Powerplant:* **1 x Allison V-1710-81**
Length: **10.16m (33ft 4in)**	*Armament:* **6 x 0.50in MG**
Span: **11.37m (37ft 3.5in)**	*Bomb load:* **680kg (1500lb)**
Height: **3.23m (10ft 7in)**	*First flight:* **Not Given**
Maximum speed: **552km/h (343mph)**	*Initial climb:* **646m (2120ft) per min**
Service ceiling: **9450m (31,000ft)**	*Weight (empty):* **2812kg (6200lb)**
Range: **1207km (750 miles)**	*Weight (loaded):* **5171kg (11,400lb)**

CURTISS P-40 (TOMAHAWK MK I)

SPECIFICATIONS

CURTISS P-40B (TOMAHAWK MK I)

Manufacturer: **Curtiss-Wright Corp.**	Crew: **One**
Type: **(P-40B) Fighter**	Powerplant: **1 x Allison V-1710-33**
Length: **9.66 m (31ft 8.5in)**	Armament: **4 x MG**
Span: **11.37m (37ft 3.5in)**	Bomb load: **None**
Height: **3.22m (10ft 7in)**	First flight: **January 1940**
Maximum speed: **567km/h (352mph)**	Initial climb: **807m (2650ft) per min**
Service ceiling: **9875m (32,400ft)**	Weight (empty): **2536kg (5590lb)**
Range: **1513km (940 miles)**	Weight (loaded): **3447kg (7600lb)**

In November 1934 Curtiss began the development of a new "Hawk" fighter with cantilever monoplane wing, retracting landing gear, R-1830 radial engine and all-metal construction. This was put into production as the P-36, which spawned numerous variants including the Hawk 75A export model.

More than 1300 radial-engined models were built before the decision was made to build the P-40 with a liquid-cooled Allison engine. The R-1830 engine was reliable and powerful by the standards of the 1930s, but when it became clear that it lacked the potential for development into more powerful forms Curtiss sought new means of exploiting the Model 75 airframe by installing the 775kW (1040hp) liquid-cooled Allison V-1710 Vee engine. This was particularly significant in a country where aircraft engines had become almost universally air-cooled, and predictably there were many teething troubles.

The first production model was the P-40, which entered service from May 1940. This was followed by the P-40B, P-40C, P-40D and P-40E, as well as Tomahawk Mks I, II and III for the British RAF, Australian RAAF and South African SAAF which were used as low-level army cooperation machines in Britain and as ground-attack fighters in North Africa.

CURTISS SB2C HELLDIVER

During World War II, by far the most successful Allied dive-bomber was the Douglas SBD Dauntless, which sank more Japanese shipping than any other Allied weapon. The aircraft built to succeed the Dauntless was the SB2C Helldiver, which perpetuated a name established by Curtiss with an earlier series of dive-bombers. This new monoplane had a powerful engine, large folding wing and internal bomb bay, and first flew in XSB2C-1 prototype form in December 1940. Development took a long time, partly because the prototype crashed, but mainly because the US services asked for 880 further major design changes after the SB2C-1 had been frozen for production in November 1941. Built to the extent of 7200 aircraft, including the A-25 land-based version for the US Army as well as the Canadian-built SBF and SBW, the type made its operational debut in November 1943.

In service it was never as effective as its predecessor, but fought in every major conflict of the war in the Pacific. The main models were the SB2C-1 baseline variant (978 aircraft in two sub-variants), SB2C-3 (1112 aircraft) with the 1417kW (1900hp) R-2600-20 engine, SB4C-4 (2045 aircraft in two sub-variants) with provision for additional underwing stores, and the SB2C-5 (970 aircraft) with increased fuel tankage.

SPECIFICATIONS

CURTISS SB2C HELLDIVER

Manufacturer: **Curtiss-Wright Corp.**	Crew: **Two**
Type: **Scout and Dive-Bomber**	Powerplant: **1 x Wright R-2600-8**
Length: **11.18m (36ft 8in)**	Armament: **2 x cannon, 2 x MG**
Span: **15.15m (49ft 8.26in)**	Bomb load: **1361kg (3000lb)**
Height: **4.00m (13ft 1.5in)**	First flight: **18 December 1940**
Maximum speed: **452km/h (281mph)**	Initial climb: **Not Available**
Service ceiling: **7375m (24,200ft)**	Weight (empty): **4588kg (10,114lb)**
Range: **2213 km (1375 miles)**	Weight (loaded): **7626kg (16,812lb)**

DOUGLAS A-20

SPECIFICATIONS

DOUGLAS A-20

Manufacturer: **Douglas Aircraft Co.**	Crew: **Three**
Type: **Light Attack Bomber**	Powerplant: **2 x Wright R-2600-23**
Length: **14.63m (47ft 11.88in)**	Armament: **9 x 0.50in MG**
Span: **18.69m (61ft 4in)**	Bomb load: **1814kg (4000lb)**
Height: **5.36m (17ft 7in)**	First flight: **26 October 1938**
Maximum speed: **546km/h (339mph)**	Initial climb: **355m (1164ft) per min**
Service ceiling: **7225m (23,700ft)**	Weight (empty): **7708kg (16,993lb)**
Range: **3380km (2100 miles)**	Weight (loaded): **12,338kg (27,200lb)**

As the RAF began daring low-level operations over occupied France with its Boston Mk III aircraft production of the A-20 version of the DB-7 for the USAAC was getting underway. An initial USAAC contract for the DB-7 was placed in May 1939 for 63 A-20 aircraft, which were delivered in the form of 59 P-70 night-fighters, equipped with British radar and four 20mm cannon, and three photo-reconnaissance machines. The A-20A (143 aircraft) that followed was generally similar but had unsupercharged engines and armament revised to six 3in machine-guns. The A-20B had two nose-mounted 0.50in guns and was roughly equivalent to the DB-7A; the A-20C was built to the same standard as the Boston Mk III to help standardization (this version was also supplied to the USSR under Lend-Lease).

A-20Cs undertook the first combat mission by the Eighth Air Force on 4 July 1942. A small number of A-20E conversions were completed, re-equipping A-20As with the A-20B powerplant. The most important model was the A-20G attack bomber, 2850 of which were supplied with a "solid" nose and heavier forward-firing armament, and later a dorsal turret with twin 0.50in machine-guns. There were progressive improvements to all areas and there were A-20H, A-20J and A-20K versions. Total production overall was 7385.

DOUGLAS DC-3

In 1935 Douglas designer Arthur E. Raymond planned the Douglas Sleeper Transport as an enlarged and improved version of the DC-2, with greater power and accommodation increased to 21, but he cannot have realized that as well as becoming the standard airliner of its day, it would also become the most widely used military transport ever. The prototype flew in December 1935, and the first deliveries were to civilian carriers. However, the DC-3 remains better known in its military forms as the USAAC's C-47 Skytrain, US Navy's R4D and the Royal Air Force's Dakota.

Production of these and other military variants in the USA totalled some 10,050 aircraft. The vast majority were the utility C-47 version with a strengthened cargo floor and large double doors, although there were some oddities, such as a glider version and a float-equipped version. The Soviet Union built the aircraft as the Li-2 in numbers totalling more than 2700 aircraft. These aircraft were truly war-winning weapons; Eisenhower said that along with the Jeep, the Bazooka and the Sherman tank, the C-47 had been one of the four decisive weapons of World War II, for it provided the Allies with an unparalleled transport capability that expanded into paratroop and glider-towing capabilities as World War II progressed.

SPECIFICATIONS

DOUGLAS DC-3

Manufacturer: **Douglas Aircraft Co.**	Crew: **2/3**
Type: **Transport**	Powerplant: **2 x P & W R-1830-92**
Length: **19.63m (64ft 5.5in)**	Armament: **None**
Span: **28.90m (95ft 0in)**	Bomb load: **None**
Height: **5.20m (16ft 11in)**	First flight: **17 December 1935**
Maximum speed: **370km/h (230mph)**	Initial climb: **366m (1200ft) per min**
Service ceiling: **7315m (24,000ft)**	Weight (empty): **8103kg (17,865lb)**
Range: **2575km (1600 miles)**	Weight (loaded): **14,061kg (31,000lb)**

DOUGLAS SBD DAUNTLESS

SPECIFICATIONS

DOUGLAS SBD DAUNTLESS

Manufacturer:
Douglas Aircraft Co.

Crew:
Two

Type:
Scout and Dive-Bomber

Powerplant:
1 x Wright R-1820-60

Length:
10.09m (33ft 1.25in)

Armament:
4 x MG

Span:
12.66m (41ft 6.38in)

Bomb load:
1021kg (2250lb)

Height:
4.14m (13ft 7in)

First flight:
23 July 1938

Maximum speed:
410km/h (255mph)

Initial climb:
457m (1500ft) per min

Service ceiling:
7780m (25,530ft)

Weight (empty):
2905kg (6404lb)

Range:
2519km (1565 miles)

Weight (loaded):
4853kg (10,700lb)

Undeniably the best American dive-bomber of the war, the SBD Dauntless was developed by Northrop and its chief designer Ed Heinemann in 1934 for the American carrier fleet then under construction. The resulting BT-1 design was based on the established Northrop A-17A, and 54 were delivered to the US Navy from November 1937. Features of the aircraft were large perforated split flaps and main gears that retracted back into large fairings. The last aircraft was delivered in October 1938, in much modified form, as the BT-2, with inward-retracting main wheels, a 746kW (1000hp) Cyclone engine and many refinements. Northrop had by this time become part of Douglas Aircraft and production aircraft were designated SBD-1. From June 1940 until it was retired four years later this was one of the most important US types, playing a decisive role at Coral Sea, Midway and the Solomons – despite the fact that it possessed indifferent performance and poor manoeuvrability. The main production models were the SBD-1 (57) with the 746kW (1000hp) R-1820-32 engine, SBD-2 (87) with more armament and fuel, SBD-3 (584) with better machine-guns, self-sealing fuel tankage and 24- rather than 12-volt electrics, SBD-4 (780) with detail improvements, SBD-5 (3025) with greater power, and SBD-6 (451) with a 1007kW (1350hp) R-1820-66 engine.

GRUMMAN TBF AVENGER

As the US Navy's Pacific campaign progressed a very real need for effective torpedo bombers was exposed and in response Grumman design staff under Bill Schwendler quickly developed the TBF Avenger. Two were ordered in April 1940 and the first of two XTBF-1 prototypes made the type's maiden flight in August 1941. Service deliveries began in January 1942, and large numbers were in service in time for the type to make a disastrous combat debut at the Battle of Midway in June 1942. Nevertheless, the TBF rapidly matured as the classic torpedo-bomber of World War II and proved to be a robust and well-equipped aircraft.

Production of the TBF-1 model (the only model that was built) included sub-variants such as the winterized TBF-1J Avenger, TBF-1P photo-reconnaissance type, TBF-1B for the Fleet Air Arm in the UK, TBF-1C with two 0.50in machine-guns in the leading edges of the wing, TBF-1CP photo-reconnaissance type, TBF-1D for the anti-submarine role with radar and underwing rockets, TBF-1E with podded air-to-surface radar, and TBF-1L with a powerful retractable searchlight for night illumination of surface vessels. Production was also undertaken by General Motors Corporation, which produced 7546 of the TBM model in a number of sub-variants, including the TBM-3D with anti-submarine radar.

SPECIFICATIONS

GRUMMAN TBF AVENGER

Manufacturer: **Grumman Aircraft**	Crew: **Three**
Type: **Torpedo-Bomber**	Powerplant: **1 x Wright R-2600-8**
Length: **12.42m (40ft 9in)**	Armament: **4 x MG**
Span: **16.51m (54ft 2in)**	Bomb load: **1134kg (2500lb)**
Height: **4.19m (13ft 9in)**	First flight: **1 August 1941**
Maximum speed: **414km/h (257mph)**	Initial climb: **235m (770ft) per min**
Service ceiling: **6525m (21,400ft)**	Weight (empty): **4788kg (10,555lb)**
Range: **4321km (2685 miles)**	Weight (loaded): **7876kg (17,364lb)**

GRUMMAN F4F WILDCAT

SPECIFICATIONS

GRUMMAN F4F WILDCAT

Manufacturer: **Grumman Aircraft**	Crew: **One**
Type: **Fighter, Fighter-Bomber**	Powerplant: **1 x P & W R-1830-86**
Length: **8.76m (28ft 9in)**	Armament: **6 x 0.50in**
Span: **11.58m (38ft 0in)**	Bomb load: **91kg (200lb)**
Height: **2.81m (9ft 2.5in)**	First flight: **2 September 1937**
Maximum speed: **512km/h (318mph)**	Initial climb: **594m (1950ft) per min**
Service ceiling: **10,365m (34,000ft)**	Weight (empty): **2612kg (5758lb)**
Range: **2012km (1250 miles)**	Weight (loaded): **3607kg (7952lb)**

Designed as a biplane to continue Grumman's very successful F3F series of single-seat carrier fighters, the XF4F-1 biplane was replanned on the drawing board in summer 1936 as a mid-wing monoplane (XF4F-2), first flying in September 1937. It lost out to the Brewster Buffalo in the US Navy fighter competition, but Grumman continued to develop it as the XF4-3 with a more powerful engine, and in early 1939 received an order from the French Aeronavale for 100, the US Navy following with 54 in August. The French aircraft were subsequently diverted to Britain, where they became Martlet Is.

Eventually 284 F4F-3 production aircraft were built, with the R-1830-76 engine. Production built up with both Twin Wasp and Cyclone engines, and included the F4F-3A (95 aircraft), F4F-4 with manually folding wing tips (1144 aircraft) and unarmed photo-reconnaissance F4F-7 (21 aircraft). General Motors built 1140 FM-1 (F4F-4) aircraft and the powerful 4467 FM-2 aircraft with the R-1830-56 engine and a taller fin. Some 1082 F4Fs were delivered to the UK, where the type initially known as the Martlet became the Wildcat. The F4F was the US Navy's most important fighter at the time of the US entry into the war, and was involved in early actions in the Pacific. Production continued right through the war.

LOCKHEED HUDSON

To meet a British and Commonwealth coastal reconnaissance bomber requirement outlined by the British Purchasing Commission in 1938, Lockheed produced a militarized version of its Model 14 Super Electra transport, which the British called the Hudson. The first of 351 Hudson Mk I aircraft reached the UK by sea in February 1939, and entered service in February 1939. On 8 October 1939 a Hudson over Jutland shot down the first German aircraft claimed by the RAF in the war. In February 1940 another Hudson discovered the German prison ship *Altmark* in a Norwegian fjord and directed naval forces to the rescue and over the Dunkirk beaches they were flown as dogfighters. From 1942 Hudsons made numerous clandestine landings in France to deliver or collect agents or supplies.

There were numerous models from the Mk II to Mk VI, distinguished primarily by their engines. Large numbers of Hudsons were also delivered under the Lend-Lease scheme, and variously configured for anti-shipping and submarine work with radar, rocket launchers and depth charges, and for the air-sea rescue mission with an underslung air-dropped lifeboat. Total deliveries were 2584 including about 490 armed versions for the US Army, 20 PBO (Hudson Mk IIIA) for the US Navy and 300 AT-18/-18A gunnery and navigational trainers.

SPECIFICATIONS

LOCKHEED HUDSON

Manufacturer: **Lockheed**	Crew: **Six**
Type: **Coastal Recon' Bomber**	Powerplant: **2 x GR-1820-G102A**
Length: **13.50m (44ft 3.75in)**	Armament: **7 x 0.303in MG**
Span: **19.96m (65ft 6in)**	Bomb load: **612kg (1350lb)**
Height: **3.32m (10ft 10.5in)**	First flight: **10 December 1938**
Maximum speed: **357km/h (222mph)**	Initial climb: **305m (1000ft) per min**
Service ceiling: **6400m (21,000ft)**	Weight (empty): **5484kg (12,091lb)**
Range: **3154km (1960 miles)**	Weight (loaded): **8845kg (19,500lb)**

LOCKHEED P-38 LIGHTNING

SPECIFICATIONS

LOCKHEED P-38 LIGHTNING

Manufacturer: **Lockheed**	Crew: **One**
Type: **Long-Range Fighter**	Powerplant: **2 x Allison V-1710-111**
Length: **11.53m (37ft 10in)**	Armament: **1 x cannon, 4 x MG**
Span: **15.85m (52ft 0in)**	Bomb load: **1814kg (4000lb)**
Height: **3.91m (12ft 10in)**	First flight: **Not Given**
Maximum speed: **666km/h (414mph)**	Initial climb: **870m (2850ft) per min**
Service ceiling: **13,410m (44,000ft)**	Weight (empty): **5806kg (12,800lb)**
Range: **4184km (2600 miles)**	Weight (loaded): **9798kg (21,600lb)**

In February 1937 the USAAC issued a specification for a long-range interceptor (pursuit) and escort fighter, calling for a speed of 576km/h (360mph) at 6100m (20,000ft) and endurance at this speed of one hour. In response, Lockheed, which had thus far not built a purely military type, created a revolutionary fighter identified as the P-38 that bristled with innovations and posed considerable technical risks.

Powered by two Allison engines, with GEC turbochargers recessed into the tops of twin-tail booms supporting the main units of the tricycle landing gear, and with the pilot seated in the central nacelle behind heavy nose armament and the nosewheel unit, the XP-38 prototype first flew in January 1939. Much development work ensued, and despite mounting costs the aircraft demonstrated such outstanding performance that project funding continued. In August 1941 the initial operational variant, P-38D, entered service and thereafter it saw action in North Africa, northwest Europe and the Pacific. Total production was 9393 aircraft, including conversions to F-4 and F-5 reconnaissance standards. The most important fighter variants, featuring steadily more power, were the P-38E (210), P-38F (527), P-38G (1082), P-38H (601), P-38J (2970) and P-38L (3923). There were also night-fighter, trainer and bomber leader conversions.

LOCKHEED VENTURA

A direct descendant of the Lockheed Model 14, the Model 18 Lodestar first flew in September 1939 and was operated in wartime by the US Army and the RAF. A military aircraft was then developed, which Lockheed offered to the British in coastal reconnaissance and light bomber forms as successor to the Hudson and Bristol Blenheim respectively. The first Ventura Mk I flew on 31 July 1941, and together with the uprated Mk II and Mk IIIA versions entered service in November 1942 in the light bomber role. It proved vulnerable in daylight raids, and during the summer of 1943 was replaced by the Mitchell and Boston. The Ventura was retasked to the maritime role and served with distinction in the Pacific. Later models were the Ventura Mk II and Mk IIA. In American service the Ventura was known as the B-34, and served as bomber trainer (B-34A-2) gunnery trainer (B-34A-3), target tug (B-34A-4), and navigator trainer aircraft. The B-37 was an armed reconnaissance version. The US Navy operated a derivative of the Model 18 transport as the PV Ventura for the patrol bomber role. The core model was the PV-1; 1800 were built and 387 transferred to the UK as Ventura GR.Mk V machines. The US Marine Corps converted a few to night-fighters with British radar equipment, and some PV-1 machines were converted as PV-1P photo-reconnaissance aircraft.

SPECIFICATIONS

LOCKHEED VENTURA

Manufacturer: **Lockheed**	Crew: **Five**
Type: **Coastal Recon' Bomber**	Powerplant: **2 x P & W R-2800-31**
Length: **15.77m (51ft 9in)**	Armament: **6 x MG**
Span: **19.96m (65ft 6in)**	Bomb load: **2268kg (5000lb)**
Height: **3.63m (11ft 11in)**	First flight: **31 July 1941**
Maximum speed: **518km/h (322mph)**	Initial climb: **680m (2230ft) per min**
Service ceiling: **8015m (26,300ft)**	Weight (empty): **9161kg (20,197lb)**
Range: **2671km (1660 miles)**	Weight (loaded): **15,422kg (34,000lb)**

MARTIN B-10B

SPECIFICATIONS

MARTIN B-10B

Manufacturer: Glenn L. Martin Co.	**Crew:** Four
Type: Medium Bomber	**Powerplant:** 2 x Wright R-1820
Length: 13.46m (44ft 2in)	**Armament:** 3 x 0.303in MG
Span: 21.60 m (70ft 10.5in)	**Bomb load:** 1025kg (2260lb)
Height: 3.53m (11ft 7in)	**First flight:** January 1932
Maximum speed: 322km/h (200mph)	**Initial climb:** 567m (1860ft) per min
Service ceiling: 7680m (25,200ft)	**Weight (empty):** 4682kg (10,322lb)
Range: 950km (590 miles)	**Weight (loaded):** 7210kg (15,894lb)

Martin was one of the earliest important suppliers of US Army and Navy aircraft, and in 1922 General Billy Mitchell used Martin MB-2 bombers to demonstrate that battleships could be sunk from the air. After many historic aircraft ventures, Martin built the Model 123 as a company-funded venture and this aircraft may be regarded as one of the most significant advances in the history of military aircraft. It introduced cantilever monoplane wings, flaps, stressed skin construction, retractable landing gear, advanced engine cowls, variable pitch propellers and an internal bomb bay with power-driven doors. It was also the first American warplane to be fitted with turreted armament and despite having only 447kW (600hp) Cyclone engines the prototype was considerably faster than any of the pursuit fighters then in service with the US Army.

The aircraft eventually entered production as the YB-10, for service delivery from June 1934. The US Army Air Corps (USAAC) received 151 examples of the B-10 and B-12 bombers, and had retired all of them before World War II, but some of the aircraft that were exported to China and the Netherlands East Indies in the late 1930s and early 1940s fought against the Japanese, thus becoming the first American-designed bomber to be flown in combat.

MARTIN B-26 MARAUDER

With its established reputation in bomber design and production Martin made concerted efforts to win the 1939 Medium Bomber competition of the US Army, and boldly entered a design featuring a wing optimized for high cruise efficiency rather than landing. This Model 179 was ordered off the drawing board in July 1939 and first flew in November 1940. Production B-26A Marauder aircraft with torpedo shackles between the bomb doors were deployed to Australia the day after the attack on Pearl Harbor, and although inexperienced pilots found the aircraft more than a handful as a result of its high wing loading and high landing speed, once mastered the Marauder was an excellent warplane that achieved good results.

In May 1943 it began its career as the chief medium bomber of the Eighth Air Force in the European theatre, and went on to set a record for the lowest loss rate of any US bomber in Europe. The Marauder was built in a number of variants; the most important were the B-26 (201 machines), B-26A (139 machines with provision for a torpedo), B-26B and identical B-26C (1883 and 1235 machines with uprated engines and, from the 641st model built, a larger vertical tail and increased wing span), and B-26F and essentially similar B-26G (300 and 893 machines with increased wing incidence).

SPECIFICATIONS

MARTIN B-26 MARAUDER

Manufacturer: **Glenn L. Martin Co.**	Crew: **Seven**
Type: **Medium Attack Bomber**	Powerplant: **2 x P & W R-2800-5**
Length: **17.07m (56ft)**	Armament: **4 x 0.50in MG**
Span: **18.81m (65ft)**	Bomb load: **2177kg (4800lb)**
Height: **6.05m (19ft 10in)**	First flight: **25 November 1940**
Maximum speed: **507km/h (315mph)**	Initial climb: **366m (1199ft) per min**
Service ceiling: **7620m (25,000ft)**	Weight (empty): **9696kg (21,375lb)**
Range: **1609km (1000 miles)**	Weight (loaded): **14,515kg (32,000lb)**

NORTH AMERICAN B-25 MITCHELL

SPECIFICATIONS

NORTH AMERICAN B-25 MITCHELL

Manufacturer: **North American Aviation**	Crew: **Five**
Type: **(B-25C) Medium Bomber**	Powerplant: **2 x Wright R-2600-13**
Length: **16.12m (52ft 11in)**	Armament: **6 x 0.50in MG**
Span: **20.60m (67 ft 7in)**	Bomb load: **1361kg (3000lb)**
Height: **4.82m (15ft 10in)**	First flight: **January 1939**
Maximum speed: **457km/h (284mph)**	Initial climb: **338m (1100ft) per min**
Service ceiling: **6460m (21,200ft)**	Weight (empty): **9208kg (20,300lb)**
Range: **2454km (1525 miles)**	Weight (loaded): **18,960kg (41,800lb)**

Designed by a team led by Lee Atwood and Ray Rice, the B-25 Mitchell was arguably the best aircraft in its class in World War II and one of the most important US tactical warplanes of the conflict. The origins of the type can be found in the NA-40 of 1938, a company-funded project anticipating that the US Army Air Corps would require a new medium bomber. The NA-40 first flew in January 1939, but was then extensively modified into the sleeker and more powerful NA-40B to meet the definitive USAAC requirement issued in January 1939. The USAAC ordered 184 off the drawing board and received its first B-25 initial production aircraft in February 1941. Later models were the B-25A and B-25B, the former with self-sealing fuel tanks and the latter with dorsal and ventral turrets but no tail gun position.

The B-25B was used in the "Doolittle raid" of April 1942, when 16 aircraft lifted off from an aircraft carrier to bomb Tokyo. Some early concerns were expressed by pilots regarding the type's often tricky handling qualities, but these were soon dispelled and the aircraft began to make a notable impact on the air war. The B-25B was followed into service by the virtually identical B-25C and B-25D, and the heavily armed B-25G and -H anti-shipping models that were evolved for use in the Pacific theatre. In all some 9816 aircraft were completed.

NORTH AMERICAN P-51 MUSTANG

The Mustang is considered to be the best offensive fighter of World War II, and was certainly one of the key elements in the final Allied victory. In April 1940 the British Purchasing Commission concluded an agreement with North American to design and build a new fighter for the RAF. This was completed in a remarkable 117 days, but production of a prototype was held up by the failure of Allison to deliver the chosen engine. The NA-73X finally flew in October 1940 with the Allison V-1710 engine, which was also used in the 1045 examples of the P-51 and P-51A (Mustang Mks I and II) that served from April 1942 in the low-level fighter and reconnaissance-fighter roles. These were indifferent aircraft, but with the installation of the Packard V-1650 (a licence-built copy of the Rolls-Royce Merlin) the Mustang was transformed into one of the most important fighters of the war. The P-51B/C paved the way for the definitive P-51D of which 7966 were completed with a cut-down rear fuselage and clear-view "bubble" canopy, and later with increased fuel capacity and underwing provision for rocket projectiles as alternatives to bombs for the ground-attack role. Later models were the P-51H lightweight model and the P-51K, and the F-6 series of photo-reconnaissance aircraft. With drop tanks, the Mustang units in Britain were able to escort bomber formations all the way to Berlin and back.

SPECIFICATIONS

NORTH AMERICAN P-51 MUSTANG

Manufacturer: **North American Aviation**	Crew: **One**
Type: **Fighter, Fighter-Bomber**	Powerplant: **1 x Packard V-1650-7**
Length: **9.84m (32ft 3.25in)**	Armament: **6 x 0.50in MG**
Span: **11.28m (37ft 0.25in)**	Bomb load: **907kg (2000lb)**
Height: **4.16m (13ft 8in)**	First flight: **26 October 1940**
Maximum speed: **703km/h (437mph)**	Initial climb: **1060m (3475ft) per min**
Service ceiling: **12,770m (41,900ft)**	Weight (empty): **3103kg (6840lb)**
Range: **3703km (2301 miles)**	Weight (loaded): **5493kg (12,100lb)**

REPUBLIC P-43 LANCER

SPECIFICATIONS

REPUBLIC P-43 LANCER

Manufacturer: **Republic Aviation Corp.**	Crew: **One**
Type: **Fighter**	Powerplant: **1 x P & W R-1830-47**
Length: **8.69m (28ft 6in)**	Armament: **4 x MG**
Span: **10.97m (36ft)**	Bomb load: **None**
Height: **4.27m (14ft))**	First flight: **1939**
Maximum speed: **562km/h (349mph)**	Initial climb: **not available**
Service ceiling: **11,580m (38,000ft)**	Weight (empty): **2565kg (5654lb)**
Range: **1287km (800 miles)**	Weight (loaded): **3599kg (7935lb)**

The immediate predecessor to the P-47, and one of the most numerous aircraft in USAAC service in 1941, the P-43 Lancer was evolved from the Seversky P-35 aircraft designed by Alexander Kartveli before the company became Republic Aviation. The last of a production run of 77 P-35s was completed as an improved aircraft and designated XP-41; first flown shortly before the company change of identity, this was fundamentally the prototype of the Republic P-43 Lancer. After extensive testing, Republic completed another improved version and won an order for 13 evaluation aircraft under the designation YP-43. This showed a marked improvement over the P-35, leading in 1940 to a production contract for 54 aircraft (largely to keep the production line open during development of the P-47). The second and last orders were for 80 P-43As, with the more powerful R-1830-49 engine, and 125 P-43A-1s, with a further improved engine.

In 1942 the survivors were converted for use as reconnaissance aircraft as the RP-43, RP-43A and RP-43A-1, and then further modified with different camera installations as the P-43B and P-43C. A number of these were used by the Royal Australian Air Force and Chinese Nationalist forces in the Pacific theatre. The above photograph shows the aircraft in Chinese use.

REPUBLIC P-47 THUNDERBOLT

After analysing the results of air combats in Europe the USAAC set new targets for fighter performance; although he had the replacement for the P-43 already on the drawing board, Republic's chief designer Alexander Kartveli had to start again on the design of a much bigger aircraft to accommodate the new R-2800 engine that such performance demanded. Development was hampered by the difficulty in achieving sufficient ground clearance for the giant 3.65m (12ft) diameter propeller, and by the need to accommodate an inwardly retracting undercarriage and eight guns in the wing.

The XP-47B prototype first flew in May 1941, but only after protracted technical problems had been resolved was it cleared for production. The P-47B Thunderbolt entered service in April 1943, followed by the P-47C fighter-bomber and the definitive P-47D, with an uprated powerplant and, in its major sub-variant, a clear-view "bubble" canopy in place of the original framed canopy and "razorback" rear fuselage. Production of the P-47D and generally similar P-47G "razorback" model totalled 12,603 and 354 respectively. In service the "Jug" (for Juggernaut) was a tough aircraft, able to soak up punishment and dish it out as well. It bore the brunt of early escort duties and was built in larger numbers than any other fighter ever acquired by the USAAC.

SPECIFICATIONS

REPUBLIC P-47 THUNDERBOLT

Manufacturer: **Republic Aviation Corp.**	Crew: **One**
Type: **Fighter, Fighter-Bomber**	Powerplant: **1 x P & W R-2800-59**
Length: **10.99m (36ft 1in)**	Armament: **8 x 0.50in MG**
Span: **12.42m (40ft 9in)**	Bomb load: **1134kg (2500lb)**
Height: **4.44m (14ft 7in)**	First flight: **6 May 1941**
Maximum speed: **700km/h (435mph)**	Initial climb: **855m (2800ft) per min**
Service ceiling: **12,800m (42,000ft)**	Weight (empty): **4858kg (10,700lb)**
Range: **2776km (1725 miles)**	Weight (loaded): **7355kg (16,200lb)**

VOUGHT F4U CORSAIR

SPECIFICATIONS

VOUGHT F4U CORSAIR

Manufacturer: **Chance Vought Aircraft**	Crew: **One**
Type: **Fighter, Fighter-Bomber**	Powerplant: **1 x P & W R-2800-18W**
Length: **10.27m (33ft 8.25in)**	Armament: **6 x 0.50in MG**
Span: **12.49m (40ft 11.75in)**	Bomb load: **907kg (2000lb)**
Height: **4.50m (14ft 9in)**	First flight: **29 May 1940**
Maximum speed: **718km/h (446mph)**	Initial climb: **1180m (3870ft) per min**
Service ceiling: **12,650m (41,500ft)**	Weight (empty): **4175kg (9205lb)**
Range: **2511km (1560 miles)**	Weight (loaded): **8845kg (19,500lb)**

Planned by Rex Beisel and Igor Sikorsky to take the most powerful engine and biggest propeller ever fitted to a fighter, even in prototype form the Corsair was the first US warplane to exceed 640km/h (400mph) and outperformed all other American aircraft. The design incorporated an inverted gull-wing to keep span and main landing gear lengths as short as possible, and in original form it had two fuselage and two wing guns. It was later replanned with six 0.50in guns in the outer wings, each with about 490 rounds.

Planned as a carrier-borne fighter the type first flew in May 1940; service deliveries began in July 1942 and it entered operational duties with the US Marine Corps in the Solomons in February 1943, quickly gaining air superiority over the Japanese. Initially it was used only in the land-based role, as it was believed that the aircraft was unsuited to carrier operations. Certainly, the long nose and fearsome torque steer caused more than a few frights, but these were more than outweighed by the aircraft's superlative performance and its abilities in the ground-attack and close-support roles. Armed with bombs and rockets to supplement its fixed guns, the type remained in production until 1952; the main wartime variants were the F4U-1, F4U-4, Goodyear-built FG-1 and the Brewster-built F3A-1 aircraft.

ILYUSHIN Il-2 SHTURMOVIK

Comparable in terms of size, shape, weight and general performance with the Fairey Battle, the Il-2 Shturmovik (Bronirovanni Shturmovik – "armoured attacker") was by far the more successful aircraft and sustained what is known to have been the biggest production run of any aircraft in history. Throughout World War II, production from three large plants averaged about 1200 per month and topped 40,000 aircraft. Designed by the bureau of Sergei Ilyushin as a heavily armoured attack aircraft (with armour accounting for more than 15 per cent of gross weight), the BSh-2 prototype first flew in December 1939 but was found to be underpowered. With the AM-38 subsequent TsKB-57 prototypes were much improved. The type entered service as the single-seat Il-2 in March 1941 and was initially an indifferent warplane with the 1238kW (1660hp) AM-38 engine and an armament of two 20mm cannon and two 7.62mm machine-guns as well as bombs and 82mm rockets. Produced in vast numbers in 1942, it matured into a formidable ground-attack aircraft. The Il-2 was followed by the Il-2M with the AM-38F engine and 23mm cannon, the two-seat Il-2M Tip 3 that had an additional rear-facing crew position for rearward defence, and the Il-2M Tip 3M with 37mm rather than 23mm cannon for greater anti-tank capability.

SPECIFICATIONS

ILYUSHIN Il-2 SHTURMOVIK

Manufacturer:
Ilyushin

Type:
Close-Support, Anti-Tank

Length:
12.00m (39ft 4.5in)

Span:
14.60m (47ft 11in)

Height:
3.40m (11ft 1.75in)

Maximum speed:
415km/h (258mph)

Service ceiling:
6000m (19,685ft)

Range:
800km (497 miles)

Crew:
Two

Powerplant:
1 x Mikulin AM-38F

Armament:
2 x cannon, 3 x MG

Bomb load:
1000kg (2205lb)

First flight:
30 December 1939

Initial climb:
150m (490ft) per min

Weight (empty):
4525kg (9976lb)

Weight (loaded):
6360kg (14,021lb)

LAVOCHKIN La-5

SPECIFICATIONS

LAVOCHKIN La-5

Manufacturer:
Lavochkin

Type:
Fighter, Fighter-Bomber

Length:
8.67m (28ft 5.33in)

Span:
9.80m (32ft 1.75in)

Height:
2.54m (8ft 4in)

Maximum speed:
648km/h (403mph)

Service ceiling:
11,000m (36,090ft)

Range:
765km (475 miles)

Crew:
One

Powerplant:
1 x Shvetsov ASh-82FN

Armament:
2 x 20mm cannon

Bomb load:
500kg (1102lb)

First flight:
January 1942

Initial climb:
1000m (3280ft) per min

Weight (empty):
2605kg (5743lb)

Weight (loaded):
3402kg (7500lb)

The design bureau led by Semyon Lavochkin produced some of the best fighters for the Soviet air force's fleets during the war. After building the mediocre LaGG-3 in 1939 – accepted largely because it was easy to build – Lavochkin's team in 1941 urgently converted the airframe of one LaGG-3 to accept the Shvetsov M-82 radial engine. The change was ordered in August and the first of several prototypes flew in March 1942. Despite fractionally increased drag, it offered a speed increase to 600km/h (373mph) and, in particular, improved performance at height. The LaGG-3 was cancelled in May 1942, production then switching to the new machine, designated LaG-5. Within a matter of weeks this in turn was replaced on the assembly line by a further improvement, tested as a prototype in early 1942, with a new fuselage containing two 20mm guns and having a lower rear fuselage profile behind a canopy giving all-round vision. In service, this aircraft proved to be 45km/h (28mph) faster than a Bf109G-2 at lower altitude, but the German fighter could outclimb it and efforts were made to reduce its weight. Up to late 1944 some 9920 aircraft were built, in variants such as the La-5 with the 1103.5kW (1480hp) M-82A engine, La-5F with the M-82F (later ASh-82F) engine, definitive La-5FN, and La-5FN Type 41 with a metal rather than wooden wing.

MIKOYAN-GUREVICH MiG-3

In early 1938 the Soviet air force issued a requirement for a modern, high-altitude fighter to replace the Polikarpov I-15. This brought responses from a number of manufacturers, including Yakovlev and the new partnership of Artem I. Mikoyan and Mikhail I. Gurevich. Handicapped by its long and heavy engine, which held the armament to a poor level, the MiG-1 first flew in prototype form in April 1940, its only vice being an extreme tendency to swing on take-off and landing. In view of the amazing rapidity of its development this was an acceptable penalty and production soon got underway.

Some 100 aircraft were built, with an armament of one 12.7mm and two 7.62mm machine-guns, and either open or enclosed accommodation. The type was then replaced in production by the refined MiG-3, with a more powerful engine, new propeller, additional fuel tank, increased dihedral, improved protection and a rearward-sliding rather than side-hinged canopy. Despite adding extra guns on later aircraft it was no match for Luftwaffe fighters and by 1942 the type was being used for armed reconnaissance and close-support, with field modifications allowing the carriage of six RS-82 rockets or two bombs or chemical containers. The production total was 3322 aircraft delivered up to the spring of 1942.

SPECIFICATIONS

MIKOYAN-GUREVICH MiG-3

Manufacturer: **Mikoyan-Gurevich**	Crew: **One**
Type: **Fighter, Fighter-Bomber**	Powerplant: **1 x Mikulin AM-35A**
Length: **8.15m (26ft 9in)**	Armament: **3 x MG**
Span: **10.3m (33ft 9.5in)**	Bomb load: **200kg (441lb)**
Height: **2.61m (8ft 7in)**	First flight: **May 1941**
Maximum speed: **640km/h (398mph)**	Initial climb: **1200m (3937ft) per min**
Service ceiling: **12,000m (39,370ft)**	Weight (empty): **2595kg (5721lb)**
Range: **1195km (742 miles)**	Weight (loaded): **3350kg (7385lb)**

PETLYAKOV Pe-2

SPECIFICATIONS

PETLYAKOV Pe-2

Manufacturer:
Petlyakov

Crew:
Three

Type:
Multi-Role Attack Bomber

Powerplant:
2 x Klimov VK-105RA

Length:
12.66m (41ft 6.5in)

Armament:
4 x 7.62mm MG

Span:
17.16m (56ft 3.7in)

Bomb load:
1600kg (3527lb)

Height:
4.00m (13ft 1.5in)

First flight:
1939

Maximum speed:
540km/h (335mph)

Initial climb:
436m (1430ft) per min

Service ceiling:
8800m (28,870ft)

Weight (empty):
5870kg (12,943lb)

Range:
1500km (932 miles)

Weight (loaded):
8495kg (18,728lb)

Not until after the war did Western observers begin to appreciate the Pe-2. Built throughout the war, it was one of the outstanding Allied combat aircraft – the Soviet counterpart of the de Havilland Mosquito and Junkers Ju 88. By dint of continual improvement it remained in the front line right up to the German surrender. It was originally planned by Vladimir Petlyakov's team in 1938 as a high-altitude fighter designated VI-100. The prototype flew in 1939–40, but it was then revised as the PB-100 dive-bomber with three rather than two crew in unpressurized accommodation, a powerplant optimized for lower-altitude operations, and different armament. Level bombing at height proved inaccurate, so dive brakes were added and in June 1940 the decision was taken for the PB-100 to be placed in immediate production as the Pe-2 multi-role dive- and attack bomber. This version was supplanted from spring 1942 by the Pe-2FT optimized for fighting with uprated armament, and by replacing the underwing dive brakes with manoeuvre flaps, reduction of the nose glazing and on later aircraft an uprated powerplant. Versions of the Pe-2 were also used for long-range photo-reconnaissance and training. The final Pe-3 multi-purpose fighter version had cannon, machine-guns and underwing provision for rockets. Some 11,427 were built overall.

PETLYAKOV Pe-8

Despite its enormous industrial capacity, and a wealth of highly talented engineers, the Soviet Union was unable to put an effective strategic bomber into production during the war. The only aircraft of this type that entered service was the Petlyakov Pe-8 (identified until 1941 as the Tupolev TB-7). The project began in 1934 with a team led by Vladimir Petlyakov in the design bureau of Andreas Tupolev, who went on to make his name with the medium bombers that served throughout the war. The new aircraft was based on a specification that required optimum performance at a height of 8000m (26,240ft). This requirement proved a constant hindrance, as at the time engines capable of giving sufficient power simply did not exist. The solution was found by fitting four 820kW (1100hp) M-105 engines supercharged by a large blower in the rear fuselage. This was undoubtedly complicated but it worked: in December 1936 it flew and performed brilliantly. This achievement proved unnecessary when it was decided, just as production started in 1939, that the engines should be replaced by AM 35As which did not need the supercharger. It entered service in 1940, but did not make its combat debut until summer 1941; Soviet military planners always placed emphasis on attack aircraft for use in tactical rather than strategic roles.

SPECIFICATIONS

PETLYAKOV Pe-8

Manufacturer: **Tupolev**	Crew: **10**
Type: **Heavy Bomber**	Powerplant: **4 x Mikulin AM-35A**
Length: **22.49m (73ft 9in)**	Armament: **2 x cannon, 3 x MG**
Span: **39.94m (131ft)**	Bomb load: **4000kg (8818lb)**
Height: **6.1m (20ft)**	First flight: **27 December 1936**
Maximum speed: **438km/h (272mph)**	Initial climb: **Not Available**
Service ceiling: **7,065m (22,965ft)**	Weight (empty): **Not Given**
Range: **5,445km (3,383 miles)**	Weight (loaded): **33,325kg (73,469lb)**

POLIKARPOV I-16

SPECIFICATIONS

POLIKARPOV I-16

Manufacturer:
Polikarpov

Crew:
One

Type:
Fighter, Fighter-Bomber

Powerplant:
1 x Shvetsov M-63

Length:
6.13m (20ft 1.3in)

Armament:
4 x 7.62mm MG

Span:
9.00m (29ft 6.33in)

Bomb load:
500kg (1102lb)

Height:
2.57m (8ft 5in)

First flight:
31 December 1933

Maximum speed:
489km/h (304mph)

Initial climb:
850m (2790ft) per min

Service ceiling:
9000m (29,530ft)

Weight (empty):
1490kg (3285lb)

Range:
700km (435 miles)

Weight (loaded):
2095kg (4619lb)

Probably influenced by "Gee-Bee" racers of the United States, Polikarpov's short and simple little I-16 fighter was almost ignored outside the Soviet Union despite the fact that in mass-produced form it was 100–120km/h (60–75mph) faster than fighters elsewhere. Designed in the 1930s alongside the biplane I-15, the I-16 was a more advanced fighter in its basic concept, with a wooden monocoque body, metal/fabric wing and variable pitch propeller. It was also the USSR's first cantilever lo-wing monoplane fighter to feature retractable main landing gear units (although the gear had to be retracted by pumping a handle 100 times!). It first flew in December 1933, revealing tricky handling characteristics – a result of its mounting a radial engine in a short fuselage. Even so it entered large-scale production (7005 aircraft excluding about 1640 two-seat trainers). It came to the fore with the Republicans in Spain where its reliability, manoeuvrability and fast climb and dive surprised opponents who called it the "Rata" (Rat). It then served against the Japanese over China and continued to be flown heroically against far superior opposition until 1942, when increasing losses forced its withdrawal. It was produced in 10 main variants between the I-16 Tip 1 with the 358kW (480hp) M-22 radial and the definitive I-16 Tip 24 with more engine power and armament.

COMMONWEALTH WIRRAWAY

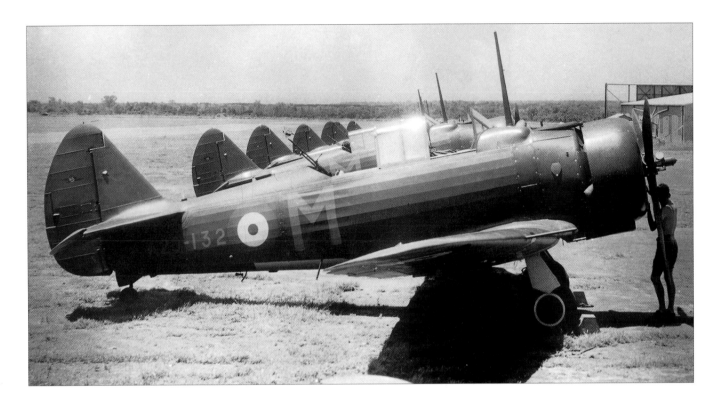

In 1936 the Australian government decided to embark on a programme to create a national aircraft industry that could eventually make Australia independent of imports, and created the Commonwealth Aircraft Corporation in Melbourne. CAC's first product was the CA-1 Wirraway, which was the Australian version of the North American NA-33, an improved version of the NA-26 advanced trainer produced for the USAAC as the BC-1. The first of two CA-1 prototypes flew in March 1939, paving the way for the Wirraway Mk I of which 755 were built in seven blocks during World War II with the factory designations CA-1 to CA-16.

The type entered service in June 1939. However, the Wirraway was by no means a combat aircraft, and when Australia suddenly found itself in the Pacific front line in December 1941 it had no modern fighters, save for a few Brewster Buffaloes supplied to the RAAF in Singapore, so Commonwealth decided to build its own, resulting in the Commonwealth Boomerang. As a result of the good performance and useful armament offered by the Wirraway it was pressed into limited operational service during 1942 in numerous roles including bomber, fighter, ground-attack plane and reconnaissance-mount, all of which it carried out with surprising effectiveness thanks to its enterprising crews.

SPECIFICATIONS

COMMONWEALTH WIRRAWAY

Manufacturer: **Commonwealth Aircraft**	Crew: **Two**
Type: **(CA-3) Trainer**	Powerplant: **1 x P & W R-1340S1H**
Length: **8.48m (27ft 10in)**	Armament: **3 x 0.303in MG**
Span: **13.10m (43ft)**	Bomb load: **None**
Height: **3.7m (12ft)**	First flight: **27 March 1939**
Maximum speed: **354km/h (220mph)**	Initial climb: **Not Available**
Service ceiling: **7000m (23,000ft)**	Weight (empty): **1811kg (3992lb)**
Range: **1150km (720 miles)**	Weight (loaded): **2991kg (6595lb)**

MONTCALM

SPECIFICATIONS

MONTCALM

Type: **Light Cruiser**	Armour (deck): **50.8mm (2in)**
Length: **179m (587ft)**	Armour (turrets): **130mm (5in)**
Beam: **17.48m (57.3ft)**	Guns: **9x152mm**
Draught: **5.28m (17.3ft)**	AA guns: **8x90mm; 8x13.2mm**
Displacement (normal): **8342tnes (8214t)**	Aircraft: **Two**
Displacement (full load): **9266tnes (9120t)**	Crew: **540**
Machinery: **Boilers & Turbines**	Launched: **October 1935**
Armour (belt): **120mm (4.7in)**	Speed: **31 knots**

Launched in October 1935 and completed in December 1937, *Montcalm* was one of six light cruisers of the "La Galissonniere" class. The ships were very well designed and mounted an excellent main armament of nine 152mm (6in) guns. They were among the best in the French Navy, which was a world leader in military ships, at the outbreak of World War II in September 1939.

On 9 September 1940, *Montcalm*, accompanied by her sister ships *Marseillaise* and *Georges Leygues*, sailed from Toulon and reached Dakar, where they played their part in repulsing an unsuccessful attempt by British and Free French forces to take over the port on 23–25 September. In February 1943, after the French Command at Dakar joined the Allies, the three cruisers went to Philadelphia for a major refit, during which radar was installed and anti-aircraft armament increased.

On 6 June 1944, *Montcalm* and *Georges Leygues* formed part of the naval support force bombarding German shore positions at Omaha Beach during the invasion of Normandy, and in August they provided support for the Allied forces landing on the French Riviera. *Montcalm* and her sister vessels *Gloire* and *Georges Leygues* had active careers in the postwar French Navy; *Montcalm* herself was stricken in 1961.

RICHELIEU

The fast, modern battleship *Richelieu* was the leader of a class of three vessels, the others being the *Jean Bart* and *Clemenceau*. Launched in January 1939, the *Richelieu* escaped to Dakar in June 1940, and, on 8 July, she was damaged in a torpedo attack by British Fairey Swordfish carrier aircraft, her captain having refused demands to surrender or immobilize his ship. Despite being stranded in port, she used her 380mm (15in) guns to good advantage in beating off an attempt to capture Dakar by a combined Anglo/Free French force in September.

In January 1943, the French at Dakar having gone over to the Allies, she sailed for the United States to be repaired and refitted. In November 1943, she served briefly with the British Home Fleet before sailing for eastern waters in March 1944. On 25 July 1944, now serving with the British Eastern Fleet, she joined British warships in bombarding Sabang. From October 1944 to February 1945, she refitted at Casablanca, and in April 1945 she sailed for a second campaign with the Eastern Fleet.

After World War II she continued to serve the French Navy, and supported the French re-occupation of Indo-China in 1945-46. Placed in reserve in 1956, she was discarded in 1960 and broken up at the Italian port of La Spezia in 1968.

SPECIFICATIONS

RICHELIEU

Type: **Battleship**	Armour (deck): **170.18mm (6.7in)**
Length: **247.87 m (813.25ft)**	Armour (turrets): **429.26mm (16.9in)**
Beam: **33.14m (108.75ft)**	Guns: **8x15in; 9x6in; 12x3.9in**
Draught: **9.67m (31.75ft)**	AA guns: **16x37mm; 8x13.2mm**
Displacement (normal): **39,116tnes (38,500t)**	Aircraft: **Three**
Displacement (full load): **48,260tnes (47,500t)**	Crew: **1670**
Machinery: **Steam Turbines**	Launched: **January 1940**
Armour (belt): **345.44m (13.6in)**	Speed: **32 knots**

BARHAM

HMS *Barham* was one of five fast battleships of the "Queen Elizabeth" class, laid down in 1912–13 to replace battlecruisers as the offensive element of the battle fleet.

Launched in December 1914 and completed in October 1915, *Barham* served with the Grand Fleet throughout World War I and saw action at Jutland, where she received six hits. Reconstructed in 1927–28, she served in the Mediterranean until 1939, when she was assigned to the Home Fleet. On 12 December 1939 she sank the destroyer *Duchess* in a collision off the west coast of Scotland. Her bad luck continued to dog her, as a fortnight later she was damaged by a torpedo from the *U30* off the Clyde estuary.

Reassigned to the Mediterranean Fleet after repair, she was damaged by gunfire from the French battleship *Richelieu* during the Anglo-French attack on Dakar, and was again damaged by air attack off Crete on 27 May 1941, during the German airborne invasion of the island. She took part in several shore bombardment operations, her 381mm (15in) guns being used to good effect against enemy installations at Bardia, Libya. On 25 November 1941 she was torpedoed three times by the *U331*, capsized and blew up off Sollum, Egypt, with the loss of 862 lives.

SPECIFICATIONS

BARHAM

Type: **Battleship**	Armour (deck): **76.2mm (3in)**
Length: **196m (643ft)**	Armour (turrets): **330.2mm (13in)**
Beam: **31.7m (104ft)**	Guns: **8x15in; 4x6in**
Draught: **10.41m (34.1ft)**	AA guns: **2x4in**
Displacement (normal): **29,616tnes (29,150t)**	Aircraft: **2–3**
Displacement (full load): **33,528tnes (33,000t)**	Crew: **1297**
Machinery: **Steam Turbines**	Launched: **December 1914**
Armour (belt): **330.2mm (13in)**	Speed: **25 knots**

BELFAST

SPECIFICATIONS

BELFAST

Type: **Heavy Cruiser**	Armour (deck): **76.2mm (3in)**
Length: **186.8m (613ft)**	Armour (turrets): **101.6mm (4in)**
Beam: **19.2m (63ft)**	Guns: **12x6in; 12x4in**
Draught: **6m (20ft)**	AA guns: **16x2pdr; 8x.5in**
Displacement (normal): **10,805tnes (10,635t)**	Aircraft: **Three**
Displacement (full load): **13,386tnes (13,175t)**	Crew: **780**
Machinery: **Steam Turbines**	Launched: **March 1938**
Armour (belt): **123.9mm (4.88in)**	Speed: **33 knots**

The cruiser HMS *Belfast* and her sister ship, *Edinburgh*, were both laid down in December 1936 and launched in March 1938. *Belfast* was the larger of the two; in fact, she was the largest cruiser ever built for the Royal Navy.

Belfast suffered an early misfortune when, in November 1939, she was badly damaged by a magnetic mine, which exploded beneath the forward engine room, breaking her back and fracturing all the machinery mountings. She returned to service in October 1942, having undergone a number of modifications, and was assigned to Arctic convoy escort duty. In December 1943 she took part in the Battle of North Cape, which culminated in the destruction of the German Navy battlecruiser *Scharnhorst*.

On 6 June 1944 she formed part of the naval force assigned to support the Allied landing on "Juno" Beach in Normandy, and on the 26th she joined other warships in bombarding German positions in the Caen area. *Belfast* continued to serve for many years postwar; she was refitted in 1963 and placed in reserve, being designated a headquarters ship in 1966. In 1971 she was preserved as a permanent memorial, being moored at Simon's Wharf on the River Thames. She continues to be a popular tourist attraction.

CENTURION

HMS *Centurion* was a dreadnought of the 1910 "King George V" class. She was laid down at Devonport in January 1911 and launched in November of that year. On 9 December 1912 she sank the Italian steamer *Derna* in a collision while on her sea trials. Completed in May 1913, she served with the Grand Fleet for the duration of World War I and saw action at the indecisive Battle of Jutland in 1916.

From 1919 to 1924 she served in the Mediterranean and the Black Sea, after which she was converted as a remotely-controlled target ship.

In 1939–40 she underwent another conversion, being modified to resemble the battleship HMS *Anson*. She retained this role until 1942, being transferred to Alexandria, and in June 1942 she made an operational sortie as part of a force running supplies through to Alexandria to Malta (Operation Vigorous). By this stage of her career, though, she was rather obsolete and very vulnerable to air attack.

She subsequently served as a floating anti-aircraft battery, being anchored south of Suez. Reduced to Care and Maintenance status, she made her last voyage in June 1944, proceeding to the English Channel to be sunk off Normandy on 9 June to form a breakwater as part of an artificial harbour.

SPECIFICATIONS

CENTURION

Type: **Battleship**	Armour (deck): **102mm (4in)**
Length: **181.2m (597.6ft)**	Armour (turrets): **279mm (11in)**
Beam: **27.1m (89ft)**	Guns: **10x343mm**
Draught: **8.7m (28.75ft)**	AA guns: **4x102mm**
Displacement (normal): **23,369tnes (23,000t)**	Aircraft: **None**
Displacement (full load): **26,112tnes (25,700t)**	Crew: **782**
Machinery: **Four Turbines**	Launched: **November 1911**
Armour (belt): **305mm (12in)**	Speed: **21.75 knots**

DUKE OF YORK

SPECIFICATIONS

DUKE OF YORK

Type: **Battleship**	Armour (deck): **152.4mm (6in)**
Length: **227m (745ft)**	Armour (turrets): **330.2mm (13in)**
Beam: **31.39m (103ft)**	Guns: **10x14in; 15x5.25in**
Draught: **9.6m (31.5ft)**	AA guns: **64x2pdr**
Displacement (normal): **38,608tnes (38,000t)**	Aircraft: **Two**
Displacement (full load): **45,517tnes (44,800t)**	Crew: **1900**
Machinery: **Steam Turbines**	Launched: **February 1940**
Armour (belt): **381mm (15in)**	Speed: **29 knots**

One of five battleships that formed the 1936 "King George V" class, the *Duke of York* – originally laid down as the *Anson* and renamed in 1938 – was launched in February 1940 and completed in November 1941, a month before her sister ship, *Prince of Wales*, was sunk by Japanese air attack off Malaya.

One of the new battleship's first tasks was to carry the British Prime Minister, Winston Churchill, across the Atlantic for a meeting with US President Franklin D. Roosevelt in December 1941. From 1942 she was employed primarily on convoy protection duties in Atlantic and Arctic waters during the Battle of the Atlantic, but in November 1942 she joined the battleships *Nelson* and *Rodney* in providing fire support for the Allied landings in North Africa.

In December 1943 her gunfire was instrumental in the destruction of the German battlecruiser *Scharnhorst* off North Cape, the enemy warship being finished off by torpedo attacks. In 1945, after a refit, she sailed to join the British Pacific Fleet, arriving in August, too late to participate in the hostilities (where she would have provided support for the invasion of the Japanese home lands). In November 1951 the *Duke of York* was laid up in reserve, and in 1958 she was broken up at Faslane, Scotland.

DUNEDIN

HMS *Dunedin* was one of a class of eight light cruisers launched at the close of, or just after, World War I. Most served in the Far East, the South Atlantic or the Mediterranean. *Dunedin* herself was launched on 19 November 1918 and was loaned to the Royal New Zealand Navy between 1924 and 1937, along with a sister ship, *Diomede*.

Reassigned to the Royal Navy before the outbreak of World War II, she formed part of the Northern Patrol from 6 September 1939, searching for enemy vessels attempting to reach Germany. In 1940 she was assigned to convoy escort duty, and in June 1941 she captured the German supply ship *Lothringen*, stationed in the Atlantic to replenish U-boats operating off Freetown, Sierra Leone. In the weeks that followed she captured two Vichy French steamers.

On 24 November, 1941, she was searching for U-boats sent to assist the German commerce raider *Atlantis* when she was sighted by the German submarine *U124* (commanded by)Lt Cdr Mohr) which torpedoed and sank her. She was the only one of her class to be lost through enemy action in World War II; the others were scrapped after the war with the exception of HMS *Dragon*, sunk as a breakwater off Normandy to form part of an artificial harbour.

SPECIFICATIONS

DUNEDIN

Type: **Light Cruiser**	Armour (deck): **25.4mm (1in)**
Length: **143.86m (472ft)**	Armour (turrets): **25.4mm (1in)**
Beam: **14m (46ft)**	Guns: **6x6in; 2x3in**
Draught: **4.87m (16ft)**	AA guns: **2x2pdr**
Displacement (normal): **4663tnes (4590t)**	Aircraft: **None**
Displacement (full load): **5811tnes (5720t)**	Crew: **450**
Machinery: **Steam Turbines**	Launched: **November 1918**
Armour (belt): **76.2mm (3in)**	Speed: **30 knots**

EDINBURGH

SPECIFICATIONS

EDINBURGH

Type: **Cruiser**	Armour (deck): **76.2mm (3in)**
Length: **18.7m (613ft)**	Armour (turrets): **101.6mm (4in)**
Beam: **19.2m (63ft)**	Guns: **12x6in; 12x4in**
Draught: **8.83m (29ft)**	AA guns: **16x2pdr; 8x.5in**
Displacement (normal): **10,805tnes (10,635t)**	Aircraft: **Three**
Displacement (full load): **13,386tnes (13,175t)**	Crew: **780**
Machinery: **Steam Turbines**	Launched: **March 1938**
Armour (belt): **124mm (4.88in)**	Speed: **33 knots**

The cruiser HMS *Edinburgh* was launched on 31 March 1938, a fortnight after her sister ship, HMS *Belfast*. Both vessels spent the early weeks of World War II searching for German blockade runners, heading homewards via the Norwegian Sea.

In 1940 her main role was convoy protection, but in 1941 she made an occasional foray into the Arctic to hunt down German weather observation ships. In May 1941 she took part in the hunt for the German battleship *Bismarck,* and in July she was deployed to the Mediterranean for convoy escort duty, remaining with the 18th Cruiser Squadron at Gibraltar for several months.

The early weeks of 1942 saw *Edinburgh* assigned to the protection of convoys sailing the Arctic route to Russia. This was a dangerous task, and it was while she was engaged in this work, on 30 April, that she was hit and disabled by two torpedoes from the *U456* (Lt Cdr Teichert). Despite this, she succeeded in inflicting severe damage on the destroyer *Hermann Schoemann,* one of a force of enemy ships sent out to attack her. One of these ships, however, hit the *Edinburgh* with another torpedo with the result that she had to be abandoned and later sunk by a torpedo from the British destroyer *Foresight* on 2 May 1942.

FORMIDABLE

The Fleet Carrier HMS *Formidable* was one of four laid down in 1937, the others being the *Illustrious, Indomitable* and *Victorious*. All three had armoured flight decks, a feature that was to save them from disaster on several occasions. Launched in August 1939 and completed in November 1940, Formidable was deployed to the Mediterranean in March 1941 and was almost immediately in action, her aircraft achieving torpedo hits on the Italian battleship *Vittorio Veneto* and the cruiser *Pola* at the Battle of Cape Matapan (26–29 March 1941). This was a British victory and somewhat of a triumph for the Fleet Air Arm.

On 26 May 1941 she was badly damaged by German bombs off Crete. She underwent repairs at Norfolk, Virginia, and in 1943 was assigned to the Gibraltar-based Force H. Her aircraft provided cover for the Allied landings on Sicily and in Italy later in the year. In 1944 she was transferred to the Home Fleet, her aircraft taking part in attacks on the German battleship *Tirpitz*.

In 1945 she sailed for the Pacific Ocean and saw action off Okinawa, being twice damaged by *kamikazes* in May near the Japanese hom,e lands. On both occasions, though, her armoured flight deck preserved her from serious harm. Placed in reserve in 1948, she was broken up in 1953.

SPECIFICATIONS

FORMIDABLE

Type: **Fleet Carrier**	*Armour (deck):* **50.8mm (2in)**
Length: **225.55m (740ft)**	*Armour (turrets):* **N/A**
Beam: **28.96m (95ft)**	*Guns:* **16x4.5in**
Draught: **8.54m (28ft)**	*AA guns:* **42x2pdr**
Displacement (normal): **23,957tnes (23,580t)**	*Aircraft:* **36**
Displacement (full load): **29,078tnes (28,620t)**	*Crew:* **1230**
Machinery: **Steam Turbines**	*Launched:* **August 1939**
Armour (belt): **114.3mm (4.5in)**	*Speed:* **32 knots**

FURIOUS

SPECIFICATIONS

FURIOUS

Type: **Fleet Carrier**	Armour (deck): **50.8mm (2in)**
Length: **239.57m (786ft)**	Armour (turrets): **N/A**
Beam: **27.12m (89ft)**	Guns: **10x5.5in; 2x4in**
Draught: **8.23m (27ft)**	AA guns: **4x2pdr**
Displacement (normal): **23,165tnes (22,600t)**	Aircraft: **36**
Displacement (full load): **27,229tnes (26,800t)**	Crew: **1218**
Machinery: **Steam Turbines**	Launched: **August 1916**
Armour (belt): **76.2mm (3in)**	Speed: **31 knots**

Launched in August 1916 and completed in June 1917, HMS *Furious* was laid down as a light battlecruiser, being converted to the role of aircraft carrier by having a hangar and flight deck installed aft. Recommissioned in March 1915, she launched the first successful carrier-borne raid on 19 July 1918, her Sopwith Camel aircraft attacking the German Zeppelin base at Tondern and destroying two airships. Missions such as these proved the viability of aircraft operating from ships, and were a foretaste of things to come in World War II.

In 1921–25 she was fully converted as an aircraft carrier, having a complete flight deck fitted, and in 1939 a small island was added in the course of a refit. During the Norwegian campaign of 1940 she flew off reinforcement aircraft, an exercise successfully repeated in the Mediterranean a year later when she provided reinforcement fighters for Malta on several occasions.

After the German invasion of Russia in June 1941 she operated in Arctic waters, her aircraft attacking German-occupied Norwegian harbour installations, and in 1944 her air group took part in the attacks on the German battleship *Tirpitz*. Her active service over, the veteran carrier was placed in reserve later in the year. She was broken up in 1948.

HERMES

HMS *Hermes* was the first vessel designed from the outset as an aircraft carrier, having a small cruiser-type hull and engines, a full flight deck and large island. Launched on 11 September 1919 and completed in February 1924, she served in the Far East in the years between the two world wars, undergoing a refit in 1933. During her career she was to see much action.

At the outbreak of World War II she was in the South Atlantic, her aircraft being involved in the attack on Dakar in July 1940. She deployed to the East Indies soon afterwards, and in February 1941, on station in the Indian Ocean, she supported the British offensive against the Italians in Somaliland. In the following months she was involved in convoy protection in the Indian Ocean and South Atlantic.

Early in 1942 she was part of the Royal Navy's Eastern Fleet, based at Trincomalee, Ceylon. On 8 April 1942, air reconnaissance reported a Japanese carrier task force approaching the island of Ceylon and *Hermes* was ordered to put to sea, along with the Australian destroyer *Vampire*, the corvette *Hollyhock* and two tankers. The ships were attacked by some 80 Japanese aircraft, and all five were sunk. *Hermes* had no aircraft on board, and was defenceless, her anti-aircraft guns proving ineffective. Over 300 of her crew perished.

SPECIFICATIONS

HERMES

Type: **Fleet Carrier**	Armour (deck): **25.4mm (1in)**
Length: **182.88m (600ft)**	Armour (turrets): **N/A**
Beam: **21.41m (70.25ft)**	Guns: **6x5.5in**
Draught: **6.55m (21.5ft)**	AA guns: **3x4in; 6x20mm; 8x.5in**
Displacement (normal): **11,024tnes (10,850t)**	Aircraft: **20**
Displacement (full load): **13,208tnes (13,000t)**	Crew: **700**
Machinery: **Boilers & Steam Turbines**	Launched: **September 1919**
Armour (belt): **76.2mm (3in)**	Speed: **25 knots**

HOOD

SPECIFICATIONS

HOOD

Type:
Battlecruiser

Length:
262.2m (860.5ft)

Beam:
32m (105ft)

Draught:
10.14m (33.3ft)

Displacement (normal):
42,774tnes (42,100t)

Displacement (full load):
46,939tnes (46,200t)

Machinery:
Boilers & Steam Turbines

Armour (belt):
304.8mm (12in)

Armour (deck):
76.2mm (3in)

Armour (turrets):
279.4mm (11in)

Guns:
8x15in

AA guns:
14x4in; 24x2pdr; 8x.5in

Aircraft:
None

Crew:
1421

Launched:
August 1918

Speed:
28.8 knots

HMS *Hood* was designed as an enlarged version of the "Queen Elizabeth" class battlecruisers in response to the German "Mackensen" class. Launched on 22 August 1918 and completed in March 1920, she was the largest warship in the world, and remained so until World War II. With a speed of 32 knots she was also one of the fastest, deck armour having been sacrificed to produce a higher speed. Much was expected of this vessel in the interwar period.

In 1923–24 she undertook a much-publicized world cruise. Her first operational sortie of World War II was to form part of a blockade across the Iceland-Faeroes-UK gap. In July 1940 she was one of the British ships that bombarded the French harbour of Mers-el-Kebir. In the latter part of 1940 she underwent a refit, during which her spotter aircraft's catapult was removed and her AA armament increased.

In May 1941, together with the battleship *Prince of Wales*, *Hood* sailed to intercept the German battleship *Bismarck* and the heavy cruiser *Prinz Eugen* in the Denmark Strait. In the running battle that followed a salvo from the battleship *Bismarck* plummeted through *Hood*'s lightly-armoured deck and penetrated into a magazine. She blew up at once and sank with the loss of 1338 crew.

INDOMITABLE

A Fleet Carrier of the "Illustrious" class, HMS *Indomitable* was launched on 26 March 1940 and completed in October 1941. In November she went aground off Jamaica while working up, delaying her deployment to the Indian Ocean, where she was to provide the air component of the Eastern Fleet.

In May 1942 she joined her sister ship *Illustrious* in attacking the Vichy French garrison on Madagascar, and in July 1943 she provided air cover for the Sicily invasion force. During these operations she was damaged by an Italian torpedo.

In July 1944 she rejoined the Eastern Fleet, and together with the Royal Navy aircraft carrier *Illustrious*, began a series of attacks on enemy communications in Sumatra. In January 1945, she sailed from Trincomalee for Sydney, Australia, with the carriers *Illustrious*, *Indefatigable* and *Victorious* to form the nucleus of the British Pacific Fleet, and in April saw action off Okinawa, where she, like many ships, was damaged in a *kamikaze* attack. She was again damaged in May, during attacks on the Sakishima-Gunto island group. On her final mission of World War II she led the task force that reoccupied Hong Kong. She underwent a major refit after the war and was placed on the reserve list in 1953, being broken up in 1955.

SPECIFICATIONS

INDOMITABLE

Type: **Fleet Carrier**	Armour (deck): **76.2mm (3in)**
Length: **243.84m (800ft)**	Armour (turrets): **N/A**
Beam: **28.87m (94.75ft)**	Guns: **16x4.5in**
Draught: **8.45m (27.75ft)**	AA guns: **16x2pdr; 10x20mm**
Displacement (normal): **22,709tnes (22,352t)**	Aircraft: **55**
Displacement (full load): **28,593tnes (28,143t)**	Crew: **1600**
Machinery: **Boilers & Steam Turbines**	Launched: **March 1940**
Armour (belt): **101.6mm (4in)**	Speed: **31 knots**

KELLY

SPECIFICATIONS

KELLY

Type:
Destroyer

Armour (deck):
12.7mm (.5in)

Length:
108.66m (356.5ft)

Armour (turrets):
12.7mm (.5in)

Beam:
10.87m (35.75ft)

Guns:
6x4.7in

Draught:
2.74m (9ft)

AA guns:
4x2pdr; 8x.5in

Displacement (normal):
1722tnes (1695t)

Aircraft:
None

Displacement (full load):
2367tnes (2330t)

Crew:
218

Machinery:
Boilers & Steam Turbines

Launched:
October 1938

Armour (belt):
19mm (.75in)

Speed:
36.5 knots

Built by Hawthorn Leslie and launched on 25 October 1938, the "K"-class destroyer HMS *Kelly* was destined to become a famous ship with a famous captain – Lord Louis Mountbatten (the exploits of the ship and her captain were made famous in the film *In Which We Serve*, which painted a rather rosy view of life in the wartime Royal Navy). She was active in the closing stages of the Norwegian campaign, covering the evacuation of Allied troops from Namsos and other locations, and on 10 May 1940, during a sortie into the Skagerrak with six other destroyers and the cruiser *Birmingham*, she was badly damaged by a torpedo from the German MTB S31 and had to be towed to Newcastle-upon-Tyne by the destroyer *Bulldog*. After repair she deployed to the Mediterranean, in which all vessels of the "K" and "J" classes served and suffered heavy losses.

Early in May 1941 she was involved in convoy escort duty and also in shelling coastal targets, notably the harbour of Benghazi. The "K" class boats were not particularly well defended against air attack, a deficiency that was to have tragic consequences when Stuka dive-bombers sank both *Kelly* and her sister ship, *Kashmir*, off the island of Crete on 23 May 1941. Of the 17 "K" and "J" class boats that served in the Mediterranean, no fewer than 12 were lost through enemy action.

KING GEORGE V

The five "King George V" class battleships were laid down in 1936–37 as replacements for the Royal Sovereign class of 1913 vintage. Apart from *KGV* herself, the others were *Anson, Duke of York, Howe* and *Prince of Wales,* the latter destined to be sunk off Malaya in December 1941.

King George V was launched on 21 February 1939 and completed on 11 December 1940. Assigned to the Home Fleet, one of her first missions was to transport Prime Minister Churchill to the United States for a meeting with President Roosevelt in January 1941 (one of her sisters also performed this mission – see page 28). In May that year she took part in the hunt for the *Bismarck,* the latter being destroyed by gunfire from the *KGV* and the battleship *Rodney. King George V* served in Arctic waters on convoy protection duty and in the Mediterranean, where she was attached to Force H to lend fire support to Allied forces landing on Sicily and at Salerno in 1943.

After a refit in 1944 she sailed to join the British Pacific Fleet. In 1945 she carried out many bombardment missions, some against the Japanese home islands; on one occasion, on 9 July 1945, she put down 267 14in shells on the Hitachi factory near Tokyo. *King George V* was decommissioned in 1949 and broken up in 1958.

SPECIFICATIONS

KING GEORGE V

Type: **Battleship**	Armour (deck): **152.6mm (6in)**
Length: **227m (745ft)**	Armour (turrets): **330.2mm (13in)**
Beam: **31.39m (103ft)**	Guns: **10x14in; 8x5.25in**
Draught: **9.6m (31.5ft)**	AA guns: **32x2pdr; 6x20mm**
Displacement (normal): **36,566tnes (35,990t)**	Aircraft: **Three**
Displacement (full load): **41,646tnes (40,990t)**	Crew: **2000**
Machinery: **Boilers & Steam Turbines**	Launched: **February 1939**
Armour (belt): **406.4mm (16in)**	Speed: **28.5 knots**

NELSON

SPECIFICATIONS

NELSON

Type: **Battleship**	Armour (deck): **152.4mm (6in)**
Length: **216.4m (710ft)**	Armour (turrets): **406.4mm (16in)**
Beam: **32.3m (106ft)**	Guns: **9x16in; 12x6in**
Draught: **10.79m (35.4ft)**	AA guns: **6x4.7in; 8x2pdr**
Displacement (normal): **36,576tnes (36,000t)**	Aircraft: **None**
Displacement (full load): **43,830tnes (43,140t)**	Crew: **1314**
Machinery: **Boilers & Geared Turbines**	Launched: **September 1925**
Armour (belt): **355.6mm (14in)**	Speed: **23 knots**

HMS *Nelson* and her sister vessel, *Rodney*, were the first British battleships to be constructed after the end of World War I, *Nelson* being launched on 3 September 1925 and completed in June 1927. Her layout was unusual – all her main guns were m,ounted forward. From 1927 to 1941 she was flagship of the Home Fleet, based at Scapa Flow in the Orkneys.

She became an early war casualty, being damaged by a mine off Loch Ewe on 4 September 1939, the day after the outbreak of war, and she did not return to service until August 1940. In the following year she was transferred to the Mediterranean, where she escorted convoys bound for the besieged island of Malta, and on 27 September 1941 she was torpedoed by an Italian aircraft during one such operation, putting her out of action until August 1942.

On 29 September 1943 the armistice agreement with Italy was signed on board her. During the Normandy landings of June 1944 she formed part of the warship force held in reserve for use if necessary by the Western Task Force, and on 12 July she was torpedoed yet again, this time by the German mtor torpedo boat *S138*. After repair at Philadelphia she deployed to the Eastern Fleet, ending her war in the Indian Ocean. She was finally broken up in 1948.

NEWCASTLE

HMS *Newcastle* was one of a class of eight British cruisers, all launched in 1936-37. The others were *Southampton, Birmingham, Glasgow, Sheffield, Liverpool, Manchester* and *Gloucester*. HMS *Newcastle*, originally laid down as *Minotaur*, was the first to be launched, on 23 January 1936.

In 1939–40 she served with the 18th Cruiser Squadron, being based mostly on the river Tyne near her home town. Later in 1940 she deployed to Gibraltar for service in the Mediterranean, and in November took part in the naval engagement with the Italians off Cape Teulada, Sardinia. In 1941 she was engaged in commerce raiding in the South Atlantic, but her main activity during 1941–42 was escorting Mediterranean convoys, providing both defence against enemy naval vessels and ground-based aircraft. This was a highly dangerous mission, especially on the Malta run.

In 1944 she was transferred to the Indian Ocean for convoy protection duties with the Eastern Fleet, her duties also including the escort of aircraft carriers attacking Japanese targets in Sumatra and elsewhere. She was still serving in the Indian Ocean when the war ended. Of the eight ships in this class, three – *Southampton, Manchester* and *Gloucester* – were lost in action in World War II.

SPECIFICATIONS

NEWCASTLE

Type: **Cruiser**	Armour (deck): **50.8mm (2in)**
Length: **180.13m (591ft)**	Armour (turrets): **25.4mm (1in)**
Beam: **19.5m (64ft)**	Guns: **12x6in; 8x4in**
Draught: **6.09m (20ft)**	AA guns: **8x2pdr; 8x.5in**
Displacement (normal): **9469tnes (9320t)**	Aircraft: **Three**
Displacement (full load): **11,725tnes (11,540t)**	Crew: **750**
Machinery: **Steam Turbines**	Launched: **January 1936**
Armour (belt): **123.95mm (4.88in)**	Speed: **32.5 knots**

QUEEN ELIZABETH

SPECIFICATIONS

QUEEN ELIZABETH

Type: **Dreadnought**	Armour (deck): **63.5mm (2.5in)**
Length: **195.98m (643ft)**	Armour (turrets): **330.2mm (13in)**
Beam: **31.69m (104ft)**	Guns: **8x15in; 4x6in**
Draught: **10.21m (33.5ft)**	AA guns: **2x4in**
Displacement (normal): **29,616tnes (29,150t)**	Aircraft: **None**
Displacement (full load): **33,528tnes (33,000t)**	Crew: **951**
Machinery: **Steam Turbines**	Launched: **October 1913**
Armour (belt): **330.2mm (13in)**	Speed: **25 knots**

The "Queen Elizabeth" class of dreadnoughts, laid down in 1912, also included the *Barham, Malaya, Valiant* and *Warspite*. A sixth vessel, *Agincourt*, was never built. *Queen Elizabeth* was launched on 16 October 1913 and completed in January 1915. She subsequently served on bombardment duty in the ill-starred Dardanelles campaign before rejoining the Grand Fleet, whose flagship she was from 1916 to 1918. However, her anti-aircaft defence was always inadequate

She served in the Mediterranean between the two world wars, undergoing substantial reconstruction in 1926–27 and again in 1937–40. She was recommissioned in January 1941 and based at Alexandria, where in December 1941 she was severely damaged in a daring attack by three Italian "human torpedo" teams, who placed explosive charges under her and her sister ship, HMS *Valiant*. She was made seaworthy and sent to Norfolk, Virginia, for repair, being recommissioned in June 1943. After a spell with the Home Fleet, she was sent to join the Eastern Fleet in the Indian Ocean, where she took part in several bombardment operations against enemy positions in Burma and Sumatra. She was broken up in 1948. She was fortunate to escape the attention of Japanese maritime aircraft, who would have found her an easy prey.

PRINCE OF WALES

Launched on 3 May 1939, the "King George V"-class battleship *Prince of Wales* was the most modern and powerful warship in the Royal Navy when she was completed in March 1941. In fact, she was not fully fitted out when, in May 1941, she was ordered to sea to hunt the German battleship *Bismarck*, and some civilian workmen were still on board. When she came up with *Bismarck* and the heavy cruiser *Prinz Eugen* in the Denmark Strait on 24 May 1941 she received seven hits, compelling her to break off the action. The battlecruiser HMS *Hood* was sunk in this engagement.

In August 1941 the *Prince of Wales* carried Prime Minister Winston Churchill to a meeting with President Roosevelt in Newfoundland; the Atlantic Charter, in which the two Heads of State agreed to co-operate in the defence of their mutual interests, was signed on board her. In December 1941, together with the battlecruiser *Repulse*, the *Prince of Wales* arrived at Singapore, the battleship flying the flag of Admiral Sir Tom Phillips. On 10 December, while searching for a Japanese invasion force, both ships were sunk by enemy bombs and torpedoes, the *Prince of Wales* losing 327 dead, including Admiral Phillips. The attack was proof of the potency of aircraft attack and the eclipse of the battleship as the capital ship of the fleet.

SPECIFICATIONS

PRINCE OF WALES

Type: **Battleship**	Armour (deck): **152.4mm (6in)**
Length: **227.07m (745ft)**	Armour (turrets): **330.2mm (13in)**
Beam: **31.39m (103ft)**	Guns: **10x14in; 8x5.25in**
Draught: **9.6m (31.5ft)**	AA guns: **32x2pdr; 16x.5in**
Displacement (normal): **35,565tnes (35,990t)**	Aircraft: **Two**
Displacement (full load): **41,646tnes (40,990t)**	Crew: **2000**
Machinery: **Steam Turbines**	Launched: **March 1941**
Armour (belt): **406.4mm (16in)**	Speed: **29 knots**

REPULSE

SPECIFICATIONS

REPULSE

Type: **Battlecruiser**	Armour (deck): **88.9mm (3.5in)**
Length: **242m (794.25ft)**	Armour (turrets): **279.4mm (11in)**
Beam: **27.43m (90ft)**	Guns: **6x15in; 9x4in**
Draught: **9.67m (31.75ft)**	AA guns: **24x2pdr; 16x.5in**
Displacement (normal): **32,512tnes (32,000t)**	Aircraft: **Four**
Displacement (full load): **38,000tnes (37,400t)**	Crew: **1309**
Machinery: **Steam Turbines**	Launched: **August 1916**
Armour (belt): **228.6mm (9in)**	Speed: **32 knots**

Launched and completed in 1916, the battlecruiser HMS *Repulse* served with the Grand Fleet for the rest of World War I but her active career was curtailed by a collision with the battlecruiser *Australia* in December 1917, in which she was damaged. She underwent a refit in 1921–22, in which her armour protection was increased and torpedo tubes added, and in 1923–24 she undertook a world cruise. She was rated as a potent maritime vessel at the time.

She again underwent a refit in 1932–36; on this occasion her superstructure was built up, an aircraft hangar and catapult were added, and her anti-aircraft armament was increased. After this she served in the Mediterranean until 1938, when she rejoined the British Home Fleet.

At the outbreak of World War II *Repulse* joined other British ships in the search for German blockade runners, and in April 1940 she saw action in Norwegian waters. In May 1941 she took part in the search for the *Bismarck*, and later in the year, together with the *Prince of Wales*, she deployed to the Far East to strengthen the defences of Singapore. It was a fatal decision, for on 10 December, while sailing to operate against Japanese forces, both ships were sunk off the east coast of Malaya by Japanese air attack.

RODNEY

One of the Royal Navy's most famous "battlewagons", the "Nelson" class battleship HMS *Rodney* was named after Admiral Lord George Rodney, a celebrated 18th-century British naval commander. She was launched on 17 December 1925 and completed in August 1927.

At the outbreak of World War II she was with the Home Fleet, imposing the blockade of Germany's merchant commerce in northern waters, and she was in action off Norway at the start of the German invasion, being damaged in an air attack.

After repairs and a refit at Boston, Massachusetts, she returned to active service in 1941 in time to take part in the hunt for the *Bismarck*, which her heavy guns helped to destroy; she was later deployed to Gibraltar for escort duty with the Malta convoys. She formed part of the support force during the Allied invasion of North Africa in November 1942, and in the following year supported the Allied landings on Sicily and in southern Italy.

During the D-Day landings in Normandy, June 1944, she was held in reserve to support the Eastern Task Force if required. However, such was the Allied supremacy during the whole invasion operation that her services were not required. She subsequently returned to escort duties, this time in the Arctic. *Rodney* was broken up in 1948.

SPECIFICATIONS

RODNEY

Type: **Battleship**	Armour (deck): **152.4mm (6in)**
Length: **216.4m (710ft)**	Armour (turrets): **406.4mm (16in)**
Beam: **32.3m (106ft)**	Guns: **9x16in; 12x6in**
Draught: **10.76m (35.3ft)**	AA guns: **6x4.7in; 8x2pdr**
Displacement (normal): **36,576tnes (36,000t)**	Aircraft: **None**
Displacement (full load): **43,830tnes (43,140t)**	Crew: **1314**
Machinery: **Steam Turbines**	Launched: **December 1925**
Armour (belt): **355.6mm (14in)**	Speed: **23 knots**

ROYAL SOVEREIGN

SPECIFICATIONS

ROYAL SOVEREIGN

Type: **Dreadnought**	Armour (deck): **50.8mm (2in)**
Length: **191.19m (624ft)**	Armour (turrets): **330.2mm (13in)**
Beam: **26.97m (88.5ft)**	Guns: **8x15in; 12x6in**
Draught: **8.68m (28.5ft)**	AA guns: **8x4in; 16x2pdr**
Displacement (normal): **28,448tnes (28,000t)**	Aircraft: **One**
Displacement (full load): **31,496tnes (31,000t)**	Crew: **910**
Machinery: **Steam Turbines**	Launched: **April 1915**
Armour (belt): **330.2mm (13in)**	Speed: **21.5 knots**

The "Dreadnought" battleship *Royal Sovereign* was launched on 29 April 1915 and completed in 1916, serving with the Grand Fleet for the duration of World War I. She underwent two refits in the years between the wars, and in 1939–41, in service with the Home Fleet, she was assigned to convoy protection in the Atlantic, also operating in the Mediterranean in 1940. In 1941 she underwent a refit and in 1942, together with four other battleships of World War I vintage, she was assigned to the Eastern Fleet in the Indian Ocean.

On 30 May 1944 she was loaned to the Soviet Union and renamed *Arkhangelsk*. Based in the Arctic, she served as the flagship of Admiral Levchenko and led a powerful escort group whose task was to meet incoming convoys and escort them to the Kola inlet. During this period she saw hard service. On 23 August 1944, for example, while escorting Convoy JW59, she was attacked by the *U711*, whose torpedoes detonated prematurely and thus turned out to be harmless.

In September 1944 the *U315* and *U313* both tried to enter the Kola Inlet to attack her, the attempts being frustrated by net barrages; another attempt in January 1945 by "Biber" midget submarines also failed. *Arkhangelsk* was returned to the Royal Navy in February 1949 and sent to the breaker's yard.

SHEFFIELD

HMS *Sheffield* was a "Southampton"-class cruiser, launched on 23 July 1936 and completed in August 1937. At the outbreak of World War II she was serving in the Home Fleet's 2nd Cruiser Squadron. In April 1940 she acted as a troop transport, carrying men of the 146th Infantry Brigade to Norway, and in August she was sent to Gibraltar to become part of Force H for operations in the Mediterranean. In May 1941 she formed part of the force that was sent out to intercept the *Bismarck*, narrowly avoiding a torpedo attack by British Swordfish aircraft, whose crews mistook her for the massive German battleship!

Reassigned to the Home Fleet, she escorted Arctic convoys to Russia, and in December 1942, she was involved in the Battle of the Barents Sea. This was a notable British victory, during which her gunfire damaged the German heavy cruiser *Admiral Hipper* and sank the destroyer *Friedrich Eckoldt*.

In December 1943, with other Royal Navy cruisers, she engaged the German battlecruiser *Scharnhorst* off North Cape, beginning the action that ended with the *Scharnhorst*'s destruction. She later escorted aircraft carriers carrying out strikes against the *Tirpitz*. *Sheffield* was actively involved in the postwar fleet, and was broken up in 1967.

SPECIFICATIONS

SHEFFIELD

Type: **Cruiser**	Armour (deck): **38.1mm (1.5in)**
Length: **180.29m (591.5ft)**	Armour (turrets): **25.4mm (1in)**
Beam: **18.82m (61.75ft)**	Guns: **12x6in; 8x4in**
Draught: **5.18m (17ft)**	AA guns: **8x2pdr; 8x.5in**
Displacement (normal): **9246tnes (9100t)**	Aircraft: **Two**
Displacement (full load): **11,532tnes (11,350t)**	Crew: **750**
Machinery: **Steam Turbines**	Launched: **August 1937**
Armour (belt): **114.3mm (4.5in)**	Speed: **32 knots**

TRINIDAD

SPECIFICATIONS

TRINIDAD

Type: **Light Cruiser**	Armour (deck): **50.8mm (2in)**
Length: **169.16m (555ft)**	Armour (turrets): **50.8mm (2in)**
Beam: **18.9m (62ft)**	Guns: **12x6in; 8x4in**
Draught: **5.79m (19ft)**	AA guns: **8x2pdr**
Displacement (normal): **9042tnes (8900t)**	Aircraft: **Two**
Displacement (full load): **10,897tnes (10,725t)**	Crew: **730**
Machinery: **Steam Turbines**	Launched: **March 1940**
Armour (belt): **88.9mm (3.5in)**	Speed: **32 knots**

HMS *Trinidad* was one of 11 "Fiji"-class cruisers, and was launched on 21 March 1940, six months after the outbreak of World War II. Her career with the navy was to be interesting.

On 29 March, 1942, while running ahead of an Arctic convoy, she encountered three German destroyers. In a confused engagement in a snowstorm she disabled the destroyer *Z26*, which later sank, but was hit by one of her own torpedoes, which went out of control after being fired to finish off the *Z26*. The submarine *U585* then tried to attack the crippled cruiser, but was sunk by the destroyer *Fury*. The *Trinidad* managed to reach the port of Murmansk, where emergency repairs were made, and on 13 May she set out in company with four destroyers for a point west of Bear Island, where she was to make rendezvous with other British warships. The Russians had promised to provide long-range fighter cover, but only a few aircraft arrived. On the following day *Trinidad* and her escorts were located by enemy air reconnaissance and subjected to torpedo and dive-bomber attacks. One of the latter, delivered by a Junkers Ju 88, hit the *Trinidad* amidships and set her on fire. Bellwoing smoke and badly damaged, the order was given to abandon ship, and *Trinidad* was sunk by the destroyer HMS *Matchless*.

VANGUARD

HMS *Vanguard*, launched on 30 November 1944, was Britain's last battleship and was basically an enlarged "King George V" type, featuring a longer hull to accommodate four twin turrets. Although at this time it was already apparent that she would not be completed before the end of the European war (in fact, she was not completed until April 1946) it was decided to finish her for service in the Pacific, should the war against Japan drag on. Some short cuts were made in her construction, including the installation of the twin 380mm (15in) guns removed from the *Courageous* and *Glorious* when these vessels were converted to aircraft carriers, but many modifications were made as building work progressed and there were inevitable delays.

When she was eventually commissioned she carried the heaviest anti-aircraft armament of any British warship – 71 40mm guns (the lessons that had been learned the hard way by the Royal Navy regarding aerial threats were integrated into this vessel). In 1947 she made headlines when she carried members of the British Royal Family on a state visit to South Africa, and after a refit she served in the Mediterranean in 1949–51, in the training role. After undergoing refits in 1951 and 1954 she was allocated to the reserve in 1956, and was finally broken up in 1960.

SPECIFICATIONS

VANGUARD

Type: **Battleship**	Armour (deck): **152.4mm (6in)**
Length: **243.84m (800ft)**	Armour (turrets): **381mm (15mm)**
Beam: **32.91m (108ft)**	Guns: **8x15in; 16x5.25in**
Draught: **9.22m (30.25ft)**	AA guns: **71x40mm**
Displacement (normal): **45,212tnes (44,500t)**	Aircraft: **None**
Displacement (full load): **52,243tnes (51,420t)**	Crew: **2000**
Machinery: **Steam Turbines**	Launched: **November 1944**
Armour (belt): **406.4mm (16in)**	Speed: **29.5 knots**

VICTORIOUS

SPECIFICATIONS

VICTORIOUS

Type: **Fleet Carrier**	Armour (deck): **76.2mm (3in)**
Length: **243.84m (800ft)**	Armour (turrets): **N/A**
Beam: **28.88 (94.75ft)**	Guns: **None**
Draught: **8.3m (27.75ft)**	AA guns: **8x4.5in; 16x2pdr**
Displacement (normal): **22,709tnes (22,352t)**	Aircraft: **50**
Displacement (full load): **28,593tnes (28,143t)**	Crew: **900**
Machinery: **Steam Turbines**	Launched: **September 1939**
Armour (belt): **101.6mm (4in)**	Speed: **31 knots**

A Fleet Carrier of the "Illustrious" class, HMS *Victorious* saw action in every theatre of World War II. She and her sisters differed from previous carriers in having an armoured hangar, which reduced the number of aircraft that could be carried but greatly increased the vessels' damage resistance level.

Launched on 14 September 1939 and completed in May 1941, *Victorious* was involved in the hunt for the *Bismarck* only days later. In August 1941 she played a key part in Operation Pedestal, a desperate attempt to run supplies through to Malta, and on several occasions she flew off replacement fighters to the island. In 1942–3 she was assigned to convoy protection duty in the Arctic, and in the following year her air group made a series of attacks on the *Tirpitz*.

In 1944 she deployed to the Indian Ocean, her aircraft attacking Japanese oil refineries at Palembang and Sabang, and in January 1945 she sailed for the Pacific, where she saw considerable action off Okinawa during the desperate Japanese defence of the island. She saw considerable service in the postwar years, being completely reconstructed in 1950–57. In November 1967 she was badly damaged by fire at Portsmouth while refitting, and the decision was finally taken to break her up in 1969.

WARSPITE

A Dreadnought of the "Queen Elizabeth" class, HMS *Warspite* probably saw more action than any other modern British warship and was one of the most important Royal Navy vessels of the war. Launched on 26 November 1913 and completed in March 1915, she fought in the Battle of Jutland in the following year, being severely damaged by 14 hits. *Warspite* was substantially reconstructed between the wars and was in action off Norway in April 1940.

Later in the year she bombarded shore targets in the Mediterranean. In March 1941, during the Battle of Cape Matapan, she and HMS *Valiant* destroyed the Italian cruisers *Zara* and *Fiume*, but in May *Warspite* was severely damaged by enemy aircraft off Crete. Returning to service in 1943, she formed part of the naval forces covering the Allied landings on Sicily and at Salerno, being severely damaged by German air-launched glider bombs during the latter operation. It was decided to effect only partial repairs on her, enabling her to be used in the Allied bombardment force covering the D-Day landings in 1944.

Her active career ended when she was damaged by a mine off Harwich on 13 June. On 23 April 1947, while en route to the breaker's yard, she went aground in Mounts Bay, Cornwall, and was broken up in situ.

SPECIFICATIONS

WARSPITE

Type: **Battleship**	Armour (deck): **76.2mm (3in)**
Length: **196.74m (645.5ft)**	Armour (turrets): **330.2mm (13in)**
Beam: **31.7m (104ft)**	Guns: **8x15in; 12x6in**
Draught: **10.05m (33ft)**	AA guns: **8x4.5in; 32x2pdr**
Displacement (normal): **31,816tnes (31,315t)**	Aircraft: **Three**
Displacement (full load): **37,037tnes (36450t)**	Crew: **1200**
Machinery: **Steam Turbines**	Launched: **November 1913**
Armour (belt): **330.2mm (13in)**	Speed: **25 knots**

BANDE NERE

SPECIFICATIONS

BANDE NERE

Type:
Light Cruiser

Length:
169m (554.46ft)

Beam:
15.5m (50.85ft)

Draught:
5.3m (17.38ft)

Displacement (normal):
5283tnes (5200t)

Displacement (full load):
7065tnes (6954t)

Machinery:
Turbines

Armour (belt):
20mm (.78in)

Armour (deck):
24mm (.95in)

Armour (turrets):
23mm (.9in)

Guns:
8x152mm; 6x100mm

AA guns:
3x37mm; 8x13.2mm

Aircraft:
None

Crew:
507

Launched:
October 1928

Speed:
37 knots

The *Bande Nere* – or *Giovanni Delle Bande Nere*, to give the ship her full name – was one of four "Guissano" class light cruisers, laid down for the Italian Navy in 1928. All were destined to be sunk in World War II. They were designed to counter large French destroyers of the "Jaguar", "Lion" and "Aigle" classes.

Bande Nere was launched on 31 October 1928 and completed in April the following year. On 19 July 1940, she and a sister ship, the *Bartolomeo Colleoni*, were engaged by the Australian cruiser *Sydney* and five destroyers in what became known as the Battle of Cape Spada; the *Colleoni* was sunk, 525 of her crew being rescued by the British destroyers, and *Bande Nere* got away after registering a hit on HMAS *Sydney*.

During subsequent operations *Bande Nere* was assigned to the 4th Division, which acted directly under the orders of the Italian Admiralty. Most of the 4th Division's activities involved convoy escort, although it did operate offensively against British Mediterranean convoys. It also undertook some minelaying, mainly in the Sicilian Channel. *Bande Nere* met her end on 1 April 1942, being torpedoed and sunk by the British submarine *Urge* off Stromboli. Though these vessels were fast, they were relatively lightly armed and their anti-aircraft defence was poor.

FIUME

Launched on 27 April 1930 and completed in
November 1931, *Fiume* was one of four "Zara"– class
heavy cruisers. All four were assigned to the Italian
Navy's 1st Division at the time of Italy's entry into the war
in June 1940.

In March 1941, with her sister cruisers *Zara* and *Pola*
and four destroyers, *Fiume* sailed from Taranto to join
other Italian warships in an attempt to intercept British
convoys heading for Greece. Much was expected by the
Italian High Command, but in the event they were to be
very disappointed. The Italian and British Fleets made
contact on 28 March, and in the ensuing battle, off Cape
Matapan, the battleship *Vittorio Veneto* and the cruiser
Pola were hit by torpedoes in an air attack by aircraft
from the carrier HMS *Formidable*.

The cruisers *Fiume* and *Zara* and the four destroyers
were detached to escort the badly damaged *Pola*, while
the rest of the Italian warships accompanied the *Vittorio
Veneto* to safety. That evening, *Fiume, Zara* and *Pole* were
detected by radar equipment on the cruiser HMS *Ajax*
and a few minutes later were engaged by the battleships
Warspite and *Valiant*. They were quickly reduced to
blazing hulks, being finished off by torpedoes. The
crippled *Pola* was also sunk before morning, together
with two of her escorting destroyers.

SPECIFICATIONS

FIUME

Type: **Heavy Cruiser**	*Armour (deck):* **70mm (2.75in)**
Length: **182.8m (600ft)**	*Armour (turrets):* **150mm (5.9in)**
Beam: **20.6m (67.58ft)**	*Guns:* **8x203mm; 16x100mm**
Draught: **7.2m (23.62ft)**	*AA guns:* **4x40mm; 8x12.7mm**
Displacement (normal): **11,685tnes (11,500t)**	*Aircraft:* **None**
Displacement (full load): **14,762tnes (14,530t)**	*Crew:* **841**
Machinery: **Eight Boilers**	*Launched:* **April 1930**
Armour (belt): **70mm (2.75in)**	*Speed:* **27 knots**

GORIZIA

SPECIFICATIONS

GORIZIA

Type: **Heavy Cruiser**	Armour (deck): **70mm (2.75in)**
Length: **182.8m (600ft)**	Armour (turrets): **150m (5.9in)**
Beam: **20.6m (67.58ft)**	Guns: **8x203mm; 16x100mm**
Draught: **7.2m (23.62ft)**	AA guns: **4x40mm; 8x12.7mm**
Displacement (normal): **11,685tnes (11,500t)**	Aircraft: **None**
Displacement (full load): **14,762tnes (14,530t)**	Crew: **841**
Machinery: **Eight Boilers**	Launched: **December 1930**
Armour (belt): **70mm (2.75in)**	Speed: **27 knots**

A sister ship of *Fiume*, *Gorizia* was launched on 28 December 1930 and completed exactly a year later. Unlike her three sisters, which were all destroyed, her operational career lasted until Italy's armistice in September 1943 (when Italy switched sides and joined the Allies). From the outset she was involved in attacks on British convoys, albeit without much success, and after the Battle of Cape Matapan, when the Italian Navy was reorganized, she formed part of the 3rd Division with the heavy cruisers *Trento* and *Trieste*. The principal task of the 3rd Division was convoy protection. She took part in the Second Battle of Sirte, and in June 1942 participated in one of the biggest battles of the Mediterranean war, when German and Italian forces combined to launch a costly attack on two convoys bound for Malta.

On 10 April 1943 she was severely damaged in an attack on Maddalena by B-24 bombers of the US Army Air Force (USAAF), and took no further part in the war. On 8 September 1943, following Italy's armistice with the Allies, *Gorizia* was scuttled at La Maddalena. Raised and refloated by the Germans, she was towed to La Spezia, where she was finally sunk on 26 June 1944 by human torpedoes manned by both British and co-belligerent Italian crews.

LANCIERE

The Italian destroyer *Lanciere* was one of the "Soldati" class, all of which were named after types of soldier (*Lancer, Carabinier, Fusilier* and so on). She was launched on 18 December 1938 and completed on 25 March 1939.

From the start of Italy's war in the Mediterranean she was active in defensive minelaying operations off the Italian coast, serving with the 12th Destroyer Division. Like many Italian warships, she woudl see rough handling at the hands of the Royal Navy. During the sea battle off Cape Teulada (Sardinia) in November 1940, for example, she was badly hit by the cruiser HMS *Berwick* and had to be taken in tow, but she was repaired and in action again early in 1941, escorting Axis convoys to Tripoli in North Africa. This was a dangerous duty, and many merchant vessels were sunk by Allied warships and aircraft.

In September 1941, accompanied by other destroyers of her class, she was once again on minelaying duties, sowing minefields to the southeast of Malta. Her eventual fate was strange. In March 1942 she was one of four destroyers that set out from Messina to escort the cruisers *Bande Nere, Gorizia* and *Trento* en route to the Second Battle of Sirte; in the course of that action on 23 March a severe storm blew up, sinking *Lanciere* and another destroyer, *Scirocco*.

SPECIFICATIONS

LANCIERE

Type: **Destroyer**	Armour (deck): **Unknown**
Length: **106m (347.76ft)**	Armour (turrets): **Unknown**
Beam: **10.2m (33.46ft)**	Guns: **5x120mm**
Draught: **4.35m (14.27ft)**	AA guns: **10x20mm**
Displacement (normal): **1859tnes (1830t)**	Aircraft: **None**
Displacement (full load): **2500tnes (2460t)**	Crew: **187**
Machinery: **Turbines**	Launched: **December 1938**
Armour (belt): **Unknown**	Speed: **39 knots**

KIRISHIMA

The "Kongo"-class battlecruiser *Kirishima* (named after a mountain in Kyushu) was launched on 1 December 1913 and completed in April 1915. In the 1930s, like others of her kind, she underwent major reconstruction and was reclassified as a battleship in preparation for the war in the Pacific Ocean. As well as having a formidable main armament, she was well equipped with antiaircraft guns.

In December 1941 she was assigned to escort the carriers whose aircraft attacked Pearl Harbor; she subsequently covered the Japanese landings at Rabaul and in the Dutch East Indies, and on 1 March 1942 she assisted in the sinking of the destroyer USS *Edsall* south of Java. In the months that followed she participated in almost all Japanese naval actions in the South Pacific. During the naval battles near the Santa Cruz islands, preceding the assault on Guadalcanal, she bore an apparently charmed life; on 25 October 1942 she experienced several near misses when Boeing B-17s bombed her and she was attacked by torpedo-armed aircraft. In November she bombarded Henderson Field on Guadalcanal in support of a Japanese invasion force. Her luck finally ran out on 15 November 1942, though, when she was sunk by the gunfire of the US battleship *Washington*.

SPECIFICATIONS

KIRISHIMA

Type: **Battlecruiser**	Armour (deck): **55.88mm (2.2in)**
Length: **214.67m (704ft)**	Armour (turrets): **228.6mm (9in)**
Beam: **28.04m (92ft)**	Guns: **8x14in; 16x6in; 8x3in**
Draught: **8.38m (27.5ft)**	AA guns: **4x40mm; 8x13.2mm**
Displacement (normal): **27,940tnes (27,500t)**	Aircraft: **Three**
Displacement (full load): **32,817tnes (32,300t)**	Crew: **1221**
Machinery: **Boilers & Steam Turbines**	Launched: **December 1913**
Armour (belt): **203.2mm (8in)**	Speed: **27 knots**

KONGO

SPECIFICATIONS

KONGO

Type: **Battlecruiser**	**Armour (deck):** **55.88mm (2.2in)**
Length: **214.57m (704ft)**	**Armour (turrets):** **228.6mm (9in)**
Beam: **28.04m (92ft)**	**Guns:** **8x14in; 16x6in; 8x3in**
Draught: **8.38m (27.5ft)**	**AA guns:** **4x40mm; 8x13.2mm**
Displacement (normal): **27,940tnes (27,500t)**	**Aircraft:** **Three**
Displacement (full load): **32,817tnes (32,300t)**	**Crew:** **1201**
Machinery: **Steam Turbines**	**Launched:** **May 1912**
Armour (belt): **203.2mm (8in)**	**Speed:** **27 knots**

The battlecruiser *Kongo* was built by the British firm Vickers-Armstrong at Barrow-in-Furness, England, and was the first ship in the Imperial Japanese Navy to be fitted with 355mm (14in) guns (her construction shows the good relationships between the British and the Japanese at this period). She was launched on 18 May 1912 and completed in August 1913. In the early weeks of World War I she took part in the search for Admiral von Spee's South Atlantic Squadron, which destroyed a British naval force at Coronel before being itself destroyed off the Falkland Islands.

Between the two world wars *Kongo* underwent two periods of reconstruction, after which she was reclassed as a high-speed battleship. After the outbreak of the Pacific war she was an active member of the fleet: she covered the Japanese landings in Malaya, formed part of the force escorting the aircraft carriers whose aircraft attacked Darwin and Ceylon, and in June 1942, as part of the 3rd Battleship Squadron, she formed a key escort element of the force that was to have invaded Midway Island. She featured in the battles of Guadalcanal, Santa Cruz, the Philippine Sea and Leyte Gulf, and on 21 November 1944 she was torpedoed and sunk by the submarine USS *Sealion* some 105km (65 miles) northwest of Keelung.

MOGAMI

The four ships of the "Mogami" light cruiser class were designed to mount the heaviest possible armament on the restricted tonnage set by the London Naval Treaty of 1930. They featured triple gun turrets and, following the example of Germany's "pocket battleships", their hulls were electrically welded to save weight. During trials, however, they proved to be unstable, and the first two ships – *Mogami* and *Mikuma* – were taken out of service for alterations.

Launched on 14 March 1934, *Mogami* and *Mikuma* both took part in the Battle of Midway in June 1942, the former being sunk and the latter severely damaged by carrier aircraft from the USS *Yorktown*. After repairs *Mogami* was returned to service in 1943, having been fitted with a flight deck on which it was intended to carry 11 seaplanes (as part of the Japanese's desperate attempt to augment their naval air power following severe losses). The cruiser was again damaged in action off the Solomons in July 1943; repaired a second time, she was back in service with the 7th Cruiser Squadron in 1944. On 25 October she was sunk by air attack at the Battle of the Surigao Strait. None of the other ships of the "Mogami" class survived the war; *Suzuya* was lost at the Battle of Leyte Gulf and *Kumano* was sunk by US aircraft in Colon Bay.

SPECIFICATIONS

MOGAMI

Type: Cruiser	**Armour (deck):** 38mm (1.5in)
Length: 200m (656.16ft)	**Armour (turrets):** 127mm (5in)
Beam: 20.5m (65.61ft)	**Guns:** 15x155mm; 8x127mm
Draught: 10.9m (35.76ft)	**AA guns:** 8x25mm
Displacement (normal): 12,599tnes (12,400t)	**Aircraft:** Three
Displacement (full load): 13,188tnes (12,980t)	**Crew:** 930
Machinery: Geared Turbines	**Launched:** March 1934
Armour (belt): 100mm (3.93in)	**Speed:** 36 knots

MUTSU

SPECIFICATIONS

MUTSU

Type:
Battleship

Length:
213.36m (700ft)

Beam:
28.95m (95ft)

Draught:
9.14m (30ft)

Displacement (normal):
34,431tnes (33,800t)

Displacement (full load):
39,116tnes (38,500t)

Machinery:
Steam Turbines

Armour (belt):
304.8mm (12in)

Armour (deck):
76.2mm (3in)

Armour (turrets):
355.6mm (14in)

Guns:
8x16in; 20x5.5in; 4x3in

AA guns:
20x25mm

Aircraft:
Three

Crew:
1333

Launched:
May 1920

Speed:
25 knots

Launched on 31 May 1920 and completed in October 1921, the "Dreadnought" battleship *Mutsu* (an ancient name for the provinces of northern Honshu) was the second warship of the "Nagato" class. She was extensively modified in two refits between the wars. In 1934–36, based at Yokosuka, she was used for long-range reconnaissance in the Pacific, gathering much information which was of great value when the Imperial Japanese Navy went to war five years later (though the activities of such a large ship seem to have totally eluded the Americans).

In June 1942, at the Battle of Midway, she was part of the Midway Support Group, which came under the direct orders of Admiral Yamamoto and also included the battleships *Nagato* and *Yamato*. In July 1942, following the abortive Midway operation, *Mutsu* was assigned to the 2nd Battleship Squadron of the First Fleet under Vice-Admiral Takasu, together with the battleships *Nagato*, *Fuso* and *Yamashiro*.

In August 1942, during the battle off the Solomon Islands that preceded the Japanese landings on Guadalcanal, she led a support group that included the seaplane carrier *Chitose*. On 8 June 1942, while at anchor in Hiroshima Bay, *Mutsu* was destroyed by an internal magazine explosion with the loss of 1222 lives.

MYOKO

Myoko was the leader of a class of 10,160-tonne (10,000-ton) cruisers, the others being *Ashigara*, *Haguro* and *Nachi*. She was launched on 16 April 1927. As with other cruiser classes of this period, the "Myokos", thanks to advanced design and shipbuilding techniques, mounted the maximum armament and achieved the highest possible speeds while conforming to the tonnage restrictions of the Washington Treaty. They were useful vessels, and would prove their worth during the campaign in the Pacific, though they all suffered at the hands of the Alllies.

During World War II the ships of this class formed the Fifth Cruiser Division. In December 1941 they participated in the Japanese landings in the Philippines, and all their subsequent operations were conducted in the area of the Dutch East Indies, Malaya. and the Philippines. On 24 October 1944, during Allied operations to recapture the Philippines, *Myoko* was torpedoed by an American aircraft and deemed to be a constructive total loss on 13 December.

Of the other ships in the class, *Nachi* was sunk by US air attack in Manila Bay in November 1944; *Haguro* was sunk by British destroyers off Penang in May 1945; and *Ashigara* was sunk in June 1945 in the Bangka Strait, Indonesia, by the British submarine *Trenchant*.

SPECIFICATIONS

MYOKO

Type: **Cruiser**	Armour (deck): **127mm (5in)**
Length: **207m (679.13ft)**	Armour (turrets): **76.2mm (3in)**
Beam: **19m (62.33ft)**	Guns: **10x203mm; 6x120mm**
Draught: **6.3m (20.75ft)**	AA guns: **8x25mm**
Displacement (normal): **12,568tnes (12,370t)**	Aircraft: **Two**
Displacement (full load): **13,594tnes (13,380t)**	Crew: **792**
Machinery: **Geared Turbines**	Launched: **April 1927**
Armour (belt): **102mm (4.01in)**	Speed: **33 knots**

NAGATO

SPECIFICATIONS

NAGATO

Type:
Battleship

Length:
213.36m (700ft)

Beam:
28.95m (95ft)

Draught:
9.14m (30ft)

Displacement (normal):
34,341tnes (33,800t)

Displacement (full load):
39,116tnes (38,500t)

Machinery:
Steam Turbines

Armour (belt):
304.8mm (12in)

Armour (deck):
76.2mm (3in)

Armour (turrets):
355.6mm (14in)

Guns:
8x16in; 20x5.5in

AA guns:
20x25mm

Aircraft:
Three

Crew:
1333

Launched:
November 1919

Speed:
27 knots

The two ships of the "Nagato" class (the other was the *Mutsu*) were laid down in the closing stages of World War one as part of the Japanese Navy's so-called "8-8" programme, which envisaged the building of eight battleships and eight battlecruisers. Launched on 9 November 1919, *Nagato* was completed in November 1920.

During substantial reconstruction work at Kure in 1934–36, her fore funnel was removed, she was re-engined and re-boilered, anti-torpedo bulges were added, the elevation of her main armament was increased to give the guns a better anti-aircraft capability (though using main guns to shoot down aircraft appears to have been a desperate measure), and a clipper bow was fitted. During the early months of the Pacific War she was flagship of the Imperial Japanese Combined Fleet, and as such she saw action at Midway and in the Battle of the Philippine Sea.

In October 1944, during the Battle of Leyte Gulf, she was damaged by aircraft bombs at Samar. She took no further part in the war, being laid up at Yokosuka, and surrendered to the Allies there in September 1945. In July 1946 she was used as a target ship for the US nuclear tests at Bikini; severely damaged in the second test, she sank on 29 July.

SHIMAKAZE

Laid down on 8 August 1941, *Shimakaze* was essentially an experimental destroyer, being fitted with engines of a new design that worked at an exceptionally high temperature and pressure, giving the ship a top speed of just under 40 knots. However, her good speed was negated somewhat by the role she was to undertake during the war.

Launched on 18 July 1942, *Shimakaze* took part in the evacuation of Japanese forces from the island of Kiska, in the Aleutians, in August 1943. October that year saw her operating in the South Pacific, covering a carrier task force operating in the area of the Solomons, and in May 1944 she was part of the Japanese naval forces tasked with the defence of the Marianas island chain. *Shimakaze*'s role remained primarily that of escorting carrier groups, which she undertook in the Battle of the Philippine Sea in June 1944.

She subsequently escorted Japanese troop convoys, and it was in this role that she met her end. On 11 November 1944, with other destroyers, she was escorting a large troop convoy attempting to land reinforcements at Ormoc, Leyte, when the naval force was subjected to heavy air attack. Four destroyers, *Shimakaze* included, were sunk, as were five transports. Only a fraction of the Japanese troops on the latter reached the shore.

SPECIFICATIONS

SHIMAKAZE

Type: **Destroyer**	Armour (deck): **Unknown**
Length: **99.5m (326.44ft)**	Armour (turrets): **Unknown**
Beam: **Unknown**	Guns: **4x120mm**
Draught: **Unknown**	AA guns: **2x7.7mm**
Displacement (normal): **1388tnes (1366t)**	Aircraft: **None**
Displacement (full load): **1703tnes (1676t)**	Crew: **148**
Machinery: **Geared Turbines**	Launched: **July 1942**
Armour (belt): **Unknown**	Speed: **39 knots**

TAKAO

SPECIFICATIONS

TAKAO

Type: **Cruiser**	Armour (deck): **76.2mm (3in)**
Length: **204.7m (671.58ft)**	Armour (turrets): **76.2mm (3in)**
Beam: **19m (62.33ft)**	Guns: **10x203mm; 4x120mm**
Draught: **10.9m (35.76ft)**	AA guns: **2x40mm**
Displacement (normal): **41,878tnes (41,217t)**	Aircraft: **Three**
Displacement (full load): **47,754tnes (47,000t)**	Crew: **762**
Machinery: **Geared Turbines**	Launched: **May 1930**
Armour (belt): **102mm (4.01in)**	Speed: **35 knots**

Launched on 12 May 1930, the heavy cruiser *Takao* was leader of a class of four, the others being *Chokai*, *Atago* and *Maya*. *Takao* was refitted and modernized in 1939–40. As part of the 4th Cruiser Squadron, she covered the Japanese landings in Malaya and on Luzon in December 1941, and also the landings in the Dutch East Indies in January 1942.

In June 1942, she formed part of the Japanese carrier force at the Battle of Midway, which saw the turn of the tide in the Pacific war. August 1942 saw her operating in the Solomons area, and in the battle for Guadalcanal her gunfire inflicted heavy damage on the US battleship *South Dakota*. In November 1943 she was severely damaged by US air attack while covering the movement of Japanese forces in the Truk/Rabaul area; on returning to active duty she formed part of the defence of the Marianas.

In June 1944 she participated in the Battle of the Philippine Sea. In October 1944, during the battle for Leyte, she was torpedoed by the US submarine *Darter*. Transferred to the Indian Ocean after repair, on 30 July 1945 she was attacked in Singapore harbour by British midget submarines and was so badly damaged by their charges that she sank. Refloated after the war, she was scuttled in the Malacca Straits in 1946.

YAMATO

The *Yamato* and her sister ship, *Musashi,* whose construction was carried out in great secrecy, were the largest and most powerful battleships ever built, and were designed to outfight – or at least compete on equal terms with – any group of enemy battleships. Four ships were planned, but the third, *Shinano,* was completed as an aircraft carrier, and the fourth was never launched.

Yamato was launched on 8 August 1940 and completed in December 1941. It was ironic that she should be obsolete even before she was launched – the day of the battleship was over. As flagship of the Combined Fleet she saw action in the battles of Midway and the Philippine Sea, being damaged by bombs from US aircraft. She received further damage on 25 December 1943, when she was torpedoed by the submarine USS *Skate* off Truk.

Yamato and *Musashi* both took part in the great air and sea battles at Leyte Gulf, *Musashi* sinking on 24 October 1944 after receiving numerous bomb and torpedo hits. *Yamato* herself was also damaged in this battle by two American bombs. On 7 April 1945 *Yamato* sailed from Japan on what was virtually a suicide mission against the Allied naval forces assembled off Okinawa, and was sunk by US carrier aircraft 210km (130 miles) southwest of Kagoshima with the loss of 2498 lives.

SPECIFICATIONS

YAMATO

Type: **Battleship**	*Armour (deck):* **198.12mm (7.8in)**
Length: **262.89m (862.5ft)**	*Armour (turrets):* **635mm (25in)**
Beam: **36.88m (121ft)**	*Guns:* **19x18in; 12x6in; 12x5in**
Draught: **10.36m (34ft)**	*AA guns:* **24x25mm; 1x13.2mm**
Displacement (normal): **64,008tnes (63,000t)**	*Aircraft:* **Five**
Displacement (full load): **72,806tnes (71,659t)**	*Crew:* **2500**
Machinery: **Steam Turbines**	*Launched:* **August 1940**
Armour (belt): **409mm (16.1in)**	*Speed:* **27 knots**

ZUIHO

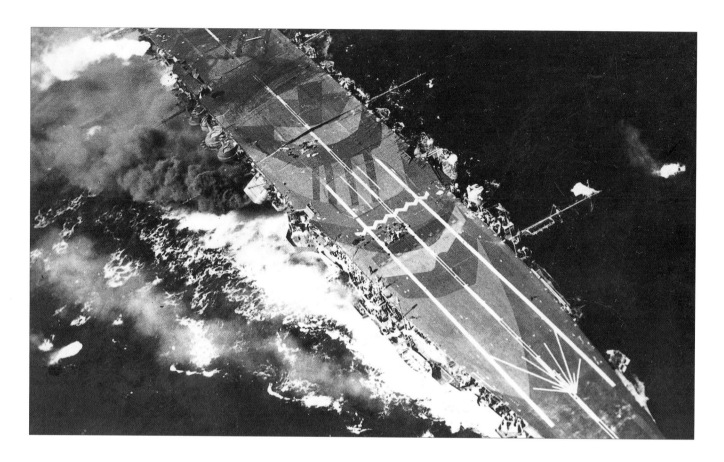

SPECIFICATIONS

ZUIHO

Type: **Aircraft Carrier**	Armour (deck): **None**
Length: **217m (712ft)**	Armour (turrets): **N/A**
Beam: **18m (59.05ft)**	Guns: **8x127mm**
Draught: **6.6m (21.65ft)**	AA guns: **15x25mm**
Displacement (normal): **11,446tnes (11,266t)**	Aircraft: **30**
Displacement (full load): **14,427tnes (14,200t)**	Crew: **785**
Machinery: **Steam Turbines**	Launched: **June 1936**
Armour (belt): **None**	Speed: **28 knots**

The light carrier *Zuiho* was originally laid down in 1935 at Yokosuka as the submarine depot ship *Takasaki*. Launched on 19 June 1936, she was re-ordered as an aircraft carrier in 1940 and renamed *Zuiho* ("Lucky Phoenix"), being completed in December that year. Her aircraft complement was not large, but she provided valuable service during the battles in the Pacific Ocean with the Americans. From the beginning, though, her anti-aircraft armament was too light.

In June 1942 her air group was to have provided close support for the Japanese invasion force in the Battle of Midway, and in September she sailed from Truk as part of the naval forces designated to support operations on Guadalcanal. However, on 26 October 1942 she was damaged by aircraft bombs at the Battle of Santa Cruz.

In April 1943 she provided reinforcements for the 11th Air Fleet on Rabaul and Buka in preparation for the last Japanese air offensive in the Solomons; further reinforcements were flown in during October. In October 1944, at Leyte, she formed part of a diversionary force under Admiral Ozawa, its task to draw the American Task Force 58 away from the main Japanese striking force. In the ensuing action, on 25 October 1944, she was sunk by US carrier aircraft northeast of Cape Engano, along with three other carriers.

ZUIKAKU

The Fleet Carriers *Zuikaku* ("Lucky Crane") and *Shokaku* ("Happy Crane") were both laid down after the expiry of the Naval Treaties of the 1930s, and consequently no limitations were placed on their design. They had strengthened flight decks, a very long range, and were capable of 34 knots. However, armament against aerial attack was rather neglected, which would prove fata.

The vessels formed part the 5th Carrier Squadron of Admiral Nagumo's 1st Naval Air Fleet, and took part in the attack on Pearl Harbor on 7 December 1941. *Zuikaku* subsequently took part in every Japanese naval action of the Pacific war up to and including the Battle of Leyte Gulf, with the exception of the Battle of Midway; her absence, and that of *Shokaku*, was due to a shortage of maritime aviation pilots and to substantial damage sustained in the Battle of the Coral Sea, where *Shokaku* received three bombs hits. *Shokaku* was sunk by three torpedoes from the US submarine *Cavalla* on 19 June 1944, during the Battle of the Philippine Sea; *Zuikaku* survived a little longer to take part in the Battle of Leyte Gulf, but on 25 October 1944 she was sunk in a massive attack by 326 American dive-bombers and torpedo aircraft, which also destroyed the carriers *Chitose*, *Zuiho* and *Chiyoda*.

SPECIFICATIONS

ZUIKAKU

Type: **Aircraft Carrier**	Armour (deck): **129.54mm (5.1in)**
Length: **257.5m (844.81ft)**	Armour (turrets): **N/A**
Beam: **28m (91.86ft)**	Guns: **16x127mm**
Draught: **8.9m (29.19ft)**	AA guns: **36x25mm**
Displacement (normal): **26,086tnes (25,675t)**	Aircraft: **84**
Displacement (full load): **32,618tnes (32,105t)**	Crew: **1660**
Machinery: **Steam Turbines**	Launched: **November 1939**
Armour (belt): **165.1mm (6.5in)**	Speed: **34.2 knots**

ALABAMA

SPECIFICATIONS

ALABAMA

Type:
Battleship

Length:
207.26m (680ft)

Beam:
32.91m (108ft)

Draught:
8.91m (29.25ft)

Displacement (normal):
35,966tnes (35,400t)

Displacement (full load):
45,923tnes (45,200t)

Machinery:
Steam Turbines

Armour (belt):
309.88mm (12.2in)

Armour (deck):
38.1mm (1.5in)

Armour (turrets):
457.2mm (18in)

Guns:
9x16in; 36x5in

AA guns:
28x1.1in; 24x40mm

Aircraft:
Three

Crew:
1793

Launched:
February 1942

Speed:
27 knots

The fourth and last battleship of the "South Dakota" class, the USS *Alabama* (BB60) was launched on 16 February 1942 and completed in August of that year. After a period of working up and convoy protection duty in the Arctic, she and the *South Dakota* arrived at Scapa Flow in June 1943, releasing two British battleships for service in the Mediterranean to cover the Allied landings on Sicily.

The two American battleships then transferred to the Pacific, forming part of Task Group 58.2, and in January 1944 they took part in attacks on Japanese bases in the Marshall Islands. *Alabama* subsequently participated in all the US Navy's main fleet actions in the Pacific, being involved in the Battle of the Philippine Sea and in actions at the Gilbert Islands, Truk, Palau, Saipan, Guam, Luzon, Taiwan, Okinawa and the bombardment of the Japanese home islands. It was a role to which the big battleships were ideally suited, especially as the Americans had almost total supremacy in the air and could give the ships protection.

On 5 June 1945 she was damaged in a typhoon off Okinawa. She was decommissioned in January 1947, but was not stricken until June 1962. She was subsequently transferred to the State of Alabama, to be preserved as a permanent memorial at the naval base of Mobile.

ATLANTA

Launched on 6 September 1941, the USS *Atlanta* was the leader of a class of 11 light anti-aircraft cruisers (the Americans had seen the dangers that enemy aircraft posed to their maritime vessels and fleets). In June 1942 she was in action at the Battle of Midway, and in August she was one of the warships covering the American landing in the island of Guadalcanal, later taking part in the sea and air battle that raged east of the Solomons as US and Japanese forces battled for possession of that strategic position.

In October 1942, as one of the cruisers providing the anti-aircraft screen for Task Force 64, she was present at the Battle of Santa Cruz, and later provided escort to the convoys carrying vital supplies to the US forces on Guadalcanal. On 6 November 1942 she sailed from Espiritu Santu as part of Task Group 62.4, escorting a troop convoy bound for the island. The convoy arrived on the 12th and began the process of disembarking, but this was halted when air reconnaissance reported strong Japanese naval forces approaching. In a series of fierce night engagements the American force was broken up, the *Atlanta* sinking in the early hours of 13 November after receiving gun and torpedo hits. The name *Atlanta* was later assumed by a cruiser of the "Cleveland-Fargo" class, launched in June 1944.

SPECIFICATIONS

ATLANTA

Type: **Antiaircraft Cruiser**	Armour (deck): **30.48mm (1.2in)**
Length: **165.5m (543ft)**	Armour (turrets): **30.48mm (1.2in)**
Beam: **16.55m (54.3ft)**	Guns: **16x5in**
Draught: **6.09m (20ft)**	AA guns: **3x1.1in; 24x40 & 14x20m**
Displacement (normal): **6096tnes (6000t)**	Aircraft: **None**
Displacement (full load): **2591tnes (8500t)**	Crew: **590**
Machinery: **Steam Turbines**	Launched: **September 1941**
Armour (belt): **88.9mm (3.5in)**	Speed: **32.5 knots**

AUGUSTA

SPECIFICATIONS

AUGUSTA

Type: **Heavy Cruiser**	Armour (deck): **76.2mm (3in)**
Length: **182.88m (600ft)**	Armour (turrets): **38.1mm (1.5in)**
Beam: **20.91m (66.25ft)**	Guns: **9x8in; 8x5in**
Draught: **7.01m (23ft)**	AA guns: **32x40mm; 27x20mm**
Displacement (normal): **9195tnes (9050t)**	Aircraft: **Four**
Displacement (full load): **12,497tnes (12,300t)**	Crew: **872**
Machinery: **Geared Turbines**	Launched: **February 1930**
Armour (belt): **76.2mm (3in)**	Speed: **32.7 knots**

A heavy cruiser of the "Northampton" class, the USS *Augusta* (CA31) was launched on 1 February 1930 and was fitted out to perform the role of flagship, as were two others of her class, *Chicago* and *Houston*.

She saw her early war service in the Atlantic, and in November 1942 she was one of the warships covering the Allied Western Task Force, landing troops on the west coast of Morocco as part of Operation Torch, the Allied invasion of North Africa. This was a relatively easy landing, with the enemy having little in the way of aircraft or naval assets.

In July 1943, as part of a plan to divert the Germans' attention from the Mediterranean, where the Allies were about to land on Sicily, she accompanied the US battleships *Alabama* and *South Dakota*, then based at Scapa Flow in the Orkney Islands, as they carried out a feint operation towards the coast of Norway, together with British battleships and aircraft carriers. In June 1944, during the Allied landings in Normandy, she was the flagship of Admiral Kirk, commanding the Western Task Force, and in August she provided fire support during the landing of the 1st Special Force on the island of Levante, off the Mediterranean coast of France. She remained in service after the war, and was finally broken up in 1960.

CHICAGO

Like *Augusta* and *Houson*, the "Northampton"-class heavy cruiser USS *Chicago* was equipped as a flagship, having extra accommodation for an admiral and his battle staff. Like most US ships of the period, she had good armament against enemy aircraft. She was launched on 10 April 1930. On 7 December 1941 she was escorting the aircraft carrier *Lexington*, ferrying aircraft to Midway Island, and so escaped the Japanese attack on Pearl Harbor.

Early in 1942 she formed part of a combined Australian, American and New Zealand naval squadron operating in the southwest Pacific, and was present at the Battle of the Coral Sea in May. In June 1942, the squadron to which Chicago belonged was designated Task Force 44 under Rear-Admiral Crutchley, RN, and in August it formed the Southern Covering Force during the American landings on Guadalcanal.

On the night of 9 August 1942, *Chicago* was badly damaged by torpedoes from Japanese warships passing through the narrows between Savo Island and Guadalcanal. After repair, she was assigned to Task Force 18, escorting supply convoys to Guadalcanal. On 29 January 1943 she was damaged in a heavy torpedo attack by Japanese aircraft, and sunk in a second attack the next day.

SPECIFICATIONS

CHICAGO

Type: **Heavy Cruiser**	Armour (deck): **76.2mm (3in)**
Length: **182.88m (600ft)**	Armour (turrets): **38.1mm (1.5in)**
Beam: **20.19m (66.25ft)**	Guns: **9x8in; 8x5in**
Draught: **7.01m (23ft)**	AA guns: **32x40mm; 27x20mm**
Displacement (normal): **9195tnes (9050t)**	Aircraft: **Four**
Displacement (full load): **12,497tnes (12,300t)**	Crew: **872**
Machinery: **Geared Turbines**	Launched: **April 1930**
Armour (belt): **76.2mm (3in)**	Speed: **32.7 knots**

DENVER

SPECIFICATIONS

DENVER

Type: **Light Cruiser**	Armour (deck): **76.2mm (3in)**
Length: **185.31m (608ft)**	Armour (turrets): **127mm (5in)**
Beam: **19.35m (63.5ft)**	Guns: **12x6in; 12x5in**
Draught: **6.7m (22ft)**	AA guns: **8x40mm; 19x20mm**
Displacement (normal): **10,160tnes (10,000t)**	Aircraft: **Three**
Displacement (full load): **14,109tnes (13,887t)**	Crew: **900**
Machinery: **Steam Turbines**	Launched: **April 1942**
Armour (belt): **127mm (5in)**	Speed: **33 knots**

One of the large "Cleveland-Fargo" class of light cruisers, the USS *Denver* (CL58) was launched on 4 April 1942. For a light vessel she was well armed, and would prove her worth during the Pacific conflict.

She went into action in the South Pacific in March 1943 as part of Task Force 68, bombarding Japanese airfields in New Georgia and participating in an action that resulted in the sinking of two Japanese destroyers. In November 1943, now assigned to Task Force 39, she was one of the warships covering the American landing in Bougainville (part of the Solomon Islands group), and in September–October 1944, with Task Force 31, she lent her fire support to the landings in the Palau group of atolls.

The provision of fire support continued to be *Denver*'s main task throughout the remainder of the Pacific war, from Leyte Gulf in October 1944 through to her final operations, the bombardment of Japanese mainland targets on Southern Honshu in July 1945.

Her bombardment actions in the interim period, covering amphibious landings while attached to various task groups, included Mindoro, Lingayen Gulf, Palawan, Mindanao and Okinawa. *Denver* survived the war despite her many major engagements, and was finally scrapped in November 1960.

DUANE

The United States Coast Guard cutter *Duane* was one of seven vessels in the "Treasury" class, so called because the ships were named after former Secretaries of the Treasury. They were large gunboats, and rendered excellent service on convoy escort duty in World War II, despite their relatively light armament and their small dimensions.

Duane was launched on 3 June 1936. One of the class, the *Alexander Hamilton*, was sunk off Reykjavik by the *U132* on 29 January 1942; the surviving boats were used as convoy flagships during up to 1944, and as amphibious force flagships in 1944–45.

Some of *Duane's* convoy escort duties took her into the Mediterranean; for example, on 19–20 April 1944 she led a strongly-escorted convoy, UGS38, through the Straits of Gibraltar.

The 87-ship convoy was heavily attacked from the air, two freighters and the destroyer USS *Lansdale* being sunk. During the Allied landings in southern France in August 1944, *Duane* was the flagship of Rear-Admiral Lowry, commanding Task Force 84. The ships reverted to gunboat status and resumed their normal coast guard duties in 1946. Remarkably, *Duane* and four other vessels of the class remained active until the 1980s, giving good service until they were retired.

SPECIFICATIONS

DUANE

Type: **Coast Guard Cutter**	Armour (deck): **None**
Length: **99.66m (327ft)**	Armour (turrets): **N/A**
Beam: **12.49m (41ft)**	Guns: **2x6pdr; 1x1pdr**
Draught: **3.81m (12.5ft)**	AA guns: **None**
Displacement (normal): **2252tnes (2216t)**	Aircraft: **One**
Displacement (full load): **2388tnes (2350t)**	Crew: **123**
Machinery: **Geared Turbines**	Launched: **June 1936**
Armour (belt): **88.9mm (3.5in)**	Speed: **19.5 knots**

ENTERPRISE

SPECIFICATIONS

ENTERPRISE

Type: **Aircraft Carrier**	Armour (deck): **None**
Length: **246.58m (809ft)**	Armour (turrets): **N/A**
Beam: **29.1m (95.5ft)**	Guns: **8x5in; 40x40mm**
Draught: **6.52m (21.4ft)**	AA guns: **16x1.1in; 25x.5in**
Displacement (normal): **20,218tnes (19,900t)**	Aircraft: **100**
Displacement (full load): **25,892tnes (25,484t)**	Crew: **2702**
Machinery: **Geared Turbines**	Launched: **October 1936**
Armour (belt): **101.6mm (4in)**	Speed: **34 knots**

The USS *Enterprise* (CV-6) was a sister vessel of the *Yorktown* and *Hornet* and was a progressive development of the *Ranger* type. She was launched on 3 October 1936 and completed in May 1938, sailing to join the US Pacific Fleet at Pearl Harbor. She was to become one of th emost famous US aircraft carriers to see action in the Pacific.

As the flagship of Task Force 8 under Vice-Admiral Halsey, she was at sea when the Japanese attacked, delivering aircraft to Wake Island. In April 1942 she escorted the USS *Hornet* on the famous Tokyo raid, when *Hornet* flew off B-25 bombers to attack the Japanese capital. During the Battle of Midway *Enterprise*'s torpedo bombers suffered terrible casualties, but her dive bombers and those of her sister ships sank three Japanese carriers, changing the course of the war. On 24 August 1942 *Enterprise* was hit by three bombs during the Battle of the Eastern Solomons, losing 74 dead, and on 26 October she took two bomb hits at the Battle of Santa Cruz, with 44 dead.

She was present at all the US Navy's subsequent Pacific campaigns, surviving two damaging attacks by *kamikazes* off Okinawa in April and May 1945. After the war she served as an attack carrier and as an anti-submarine warfare carrier, and was broken up in 1957.

HEERMAN

The USS *Heermann* (DD532) was one of the very numerous "Fletcher" class destroyers, a highly successful design that became the backbone of the US Pacific Fleet in World War II. In all, 360 were built. *Heermann* was launched on 5 December 1942 and first went into action in November 1943 during Operation Galvanic, the American landings on Tarawa and other islands in the Gilbert group (during which the US ground forces suffered grievous losses). During this operation, she gave fire support to the US 2nd Marine Division, which experienced some of the bitterest fighting of the war on Tarawa. In October 1944 *Heermann* took part in the Battle of Leyte Gulf, and in March 1945 she was part of the large number of warships escorting carriers whose air groups made the first major raid on the Japanese Home Islands. On 17 April 1945 she assisted in the sinking of the Japanese submarine *I-56* off Okinawa.

In the closing weeks of the war, she again formed part of the escort force for aircraft carriers and battleships raiding the Japanese mainland alomst at will, and in August she was at the forefront of Task Force 38, which sailed into Sagami Bay to receive the Japanese surrender. In August 1961 *Heermann* was sold to Argentina as the *Almirante Brown*.

SPECIFICATIONS

HEERMAN

Type: **Destroyer**	Armour (deck): **12.7mm (,5in)**
Length: **114.75m (375.5ft)**	Armour (turrets): **12.7mm (.5in)**
Beam: **12.03m (39.5ft)**	Guns: **5x5in**
Draught: **3.81m (12.5ft)**	AA guns: **6x40mm; 10x20mm**
Displacement (normal): **2173tnes (2050t)**	Aircraft: **None**
Displacement (full load): **2540tnes (2500t)**	Crew: **353**
Machinery: **Steam Turbines**	Launched: **December 1942**
Armour (belt): **19mm (.75in)**	Speed: **36.5 knots**

HORNET

SPECIFICATIONS

HORNET

Type:
Aircraft Carrier

Length:
246.58m (809ft)

Beam:
25.4m (83.34ft)

Draught:
6.52m (21.4ft)

Displacement (normal):
20,218tnes (19,900t)

Displacement (full load):
25,892tnes (25,484t)

Machinery:
Geared Turbines

Armour (belt):
101.6mm (4in)

Armour (deck):
None

Armour (turrets):
N/A

Guns:
8x5in

AA guns:
16x1.1in; 24x40mm

Aircraft:
100

Crew:
2702

Launched:
December 1940

Speed:
34 knots

The third vessel of the "Yorktown" class, the USS *Hornet* (CV-7) differed from her sister ships *Yorktown* and *Enterprise* in having a larger flight deck and two catapults. Laid down at Newport News in September 1939, she was launched on 14 December 1940 and completed in October 1941.

In April 1942 she leapt to fame as the carrier that launched 16 B-25 bombers, led by Lt-Col Jimmy Doolittle, to attack Tokyo. Although the raids did little material damage, they persuaded the Japanese to make further Pacific conquests in order to extend their perimeter. This resulted in over-extended supply lines on which their merchant fleet was decimated by American submarines. *Hornet* saw action at the Battle of Midway, in which her torpedo squadrons suffered heavy casualties, but her dive bombers contributed to the sinking of three Japanese carriers.

In October 1942 she provided escort to convoys resupplying the garrison on Guadalcanal, the scene of fierce fighting. On 26 October 1942, during the Battle of Santa Cruz, *Hornet* was hit by four bombs and two torpedoes, as well as two crashing aircraft, and was again damaged by another torpedo in a second attack. She was abandoned, having lost 111 of her crew, and later sunk by Japanese destroyers.

HOUSTON

The heavy cruiser USS *Houston* (CA30) was one of the six "Northampton" class vessels. Built at Newport News, she was launched on 7 September 1929. In December 1941, as flagship of the American Task Force 5, she was engaged in escort duty in the southwest Pacific, and early in February 1942 she formed part of the Allied naval forces operating off the Dutch East Indies. On 4 February the ships were sighted by a strong force of Japanese bombers, and in the ensuing attack one of *Houston*'s 203mm (8in) gun turrets was blown off (though considering the size of air fleet, she had been lucky not to have been sunk). Despite this damage she was in action later in the month, forming part of the Allied naval force under the command of the Dutch Admiral Karel Doorman.

At the end of March, in what became known as the Battle of Sunda Strait, *Houston* and other warships attempted to intercept Japanese invasion forces landing troops on Java. *Houston* and the Australian cruiser *Perth* managed to sink two large troops transports and damage a destroyer and a minesweeper, but in a fierce gun and torpedo exchange between the Allied warships and enemy cruisers and destroyers, *Houston* and *Perth* were both sunk. The Battle of the Java Sea was a complete disaster for Allied naval power.

SPECIFICATIONS

HOUSTON

Type: **Heavy Cruiser**	Armour (deck): **76.2mm (3in)**
Length: **182.88m (600ft)**	Armour (turrets): **38.1mm (1.5in)**
Beam: **20.19m (66.25ft)**	Guns: **9x8in; 8x5in**
Draught: **7.01m (23ft)**	AA guns: **32x40mm; 27x20mm**
Displacement (normal): **9195tnes (9050t)**	Aircraft: **Four**
Displacement (full load): **12,497tnes (12,300t)**	Crew: **872**
Machinery: **Geared Turbines**	Launched: **September 1929**
Armour (belt): **76.2mm (3in)**	Speed: **32.7 knots**

INDIANAPOLIS

SPECIFICATIONS

INDIANAPOLIS

Type: **Heavy Cruiser**	Armour (deck): **101.6mm (4in)**
Length: **185.92m (610ft)**	Armour (turrets): **63.5mm (2.5in)**
Beam: **20.11m (66ft)**	Guns: **9x8in; 8x5in**
Draught: **6.7m (22ft)**	AA guns: **24x40mm; 28x20mm**
Displacement (normal): **10,008tnes (9850t)**	Aircraft: **Two**
Displacement (full load): **13,970tnes (13,750t)**	Crew: **876**
Machinery: **Geared Turbines**	Launched: **November 1931**
Armour (belt): **127mm (5in)**	Speed: **32.7 knots**

The heavy cruiser USS *Indianapolis* was one of two vessels that were improvements on the "Northampton" class, the other being the USS *Portland*. Launched on 7 November 1931, *Indianapolis* fought her way through the Pacific War from the beginning almost to the very end, when she was lost literally in the last days of hostilities.

Her battle honours included the Coral Sea, Midway, the Eastern Solomons, Santa Cruz, the Gilbert Islands, Kwajalein, Eniwetok, Palau, Leyte Gulf, Midoro Lingayen, Iwo Jima, the Marianas and Okinawa, where she was damaged by a *kamikaze* attack on 30 March 1945. In addition, she took part in numerous raids on Japanese-held islands in the Pacific, 1942–44. She seemed to live a charmed life, but her luck was about to run out.

In July 1945 she transported components of the atomic bombs from San Francisco to Tinian. On the night of 29/30 July, having delivered this vital cargo, she was proceeding to Leyte when she was hit by a salvo of six torpedoes from the Japanese submarine *I-58* and sunk with the loss of all but 316 of her 1199 crew, the survivors being picked up by American flying boats and destroyers between 2 August and 8 August. Many survived the attack, only to fall victim to sharks.

JOHNSTON

The "Fletcher"-class destroyer USS *Johnston* was launched on 25 March 1943. In January 1944 she formed part of Task Force 53 under Rear-Admiral Connolly, which landed the 4th Marine Division on Roi atoll in the Central Pacific, and in July she was part of the escort for Task Group 53.2 under Rear-Admiral Reifsnider, which landed the 1st Marine Brigade and elements of the 77th Infantry Division on Guam.

During the Battle of Leyte in October 1944 she was one of seven destroyers assigned to Rear-Admiral Sprague's Task Unit 3. On 24 October, Sprague's force intercepted a force of Japanese warships attempting to escape to Leyte Gulf through the San Bernadino Strait; torpedoes from the *Johnston* and another destroyer, the *Hoel,* hit the Japanese cruiser *Kumano* and brought her to a standstill. Shortly afterwards, however, the *Johnston* and *Hoel* came under heavy and effective fire from the Japanese battleships *Yamato* and *Nagato* and both were sunk, together with the destroyer *Samuel B. Roberts* and the escort carrier *Gambier Bay.*

The Battle of Leyte Gulf, which witnessed heavy losses on both sides, was the first occasion on which organized *kamikaze* attacks were made. Like many such attacks, their psychological value was greater than the material damage they inflicted.

SPECIFICATIONS

JOHNSTON

Type: **Destroyer**	Armour (deck): **12.7mm (.5in)**
Length: **114.75m (376.5ft)**	Armour (turrets): **12.7mm (.5in)**
Beam: **12.03m (39.5ft)**	Guns: **5x5in**
Draught: **3.81m (12.5ft)**	AA guns: **6x40mm; 10x20mm**
Displacement (normal): **2083tnes (2050t)**	Aircraft: **None**
Displacement (full load): **2540tnes (2500t)**	Crew: **358**
Machinery: **Steam Turbines**	Launched: **March 1943**
Armour (belt): **19mm (.75in)**	Speed: **36.5 knots**

LEXINGTON

SPECIFICATIONS

LEXINGTON

Type:
Aircraft Carrier

Length:
270.66m (888ft)

Beam:
32.3m (106ft)

Draught:
7.34m (24.1ft)

Displacement (normal):
33,528tnes (33,000t)

Displacement (full load):
44,094tnes (43,400t)

Machinery:
Express Boilers

Armour (belt):
152.4mm (6in)

Armour (deck):
76.2mm (3in)

Armour (turrets):
N/A

Guns:
8x8in; 12x5in

AA guns:
16x1.1in; 16x.5in

Aircraft:
80–90

Crew:
1899

Launched:
October 1925

Speed:
33 knots

America's second aircraft carrier, the USS *Lexington* was originally ordered as a battlecruiser named *Constitution*, but was renamed *Lexington* in December 1917. In July 1922 she was re-ordered as an aircraft carrier (CV-2) and launched on 3 October 1925. She appeared in US Fleet exercises for the first time in January 1929, together with her sister ship *Saratoga* (CV-3). In December 1929, she made headlines when she served as a floating power plant for the city of Tacoma, Washington, following a massive power failure. Her career during World War II was to prove that aircraft carriers, now the caital ships of the fleet, could also be vulnerable to enemy aircraft.

After the Japanese attack on Pearl Harbor her air group was involved in the battle for Wake Island, followed by convoy escort duty. In May 1942 she was operating as part of Task Force 11, a joint Allied naval force formed to prevent a Japanese landing at Port Moresby, New Guinea. In the Battle of the Coral Sea, which began in the morning of 8 May 1942 after the opposing carrier task forces sighted one another and launched their respective strike forces, *Lexington* was hit by two torpedoes and three bombs and had to be abandoned, being sunk later by the destroyer USS *Phelps*. Casualties included 216 dead.

MARYLAND

The battleship USS *Maryland* (BB46) was one of a class of four, the others being the *Colorado*, *Washington* and *West Virginia*. They were built in response to a new Japanese naval construction programme, although *Washington* was not completed in order to comply with the terms of the Washington Naval Treaty. *Maryland* was launched on 20 March 1920 and completed in July 1921, joining the US Pacific Fleet in the following year.

On 7 December 1941 she was damaged in the Japanese attack on Pearl Harbor (being one of the vessels neatly lined up for the Japanese aircraft that attacked the base), and while she was undergoing repair at Bremerton her anti-aircraft armament was increased, among other improvements. This turned her into a powerful vessel.

On 22 June 1944, off Saipan, she was damaged by an aircraft torpedo which hit her in the bow, and was again damaged in a *kamikaze* attack off Leyte on 29 November, 31 crew members being killed. During the subsequent repair and refit she underwent further modification, including the replacement of her secondary armament. On 7 April 1945 she was seriously damaged by a *kamikaze* off Okinawa, effectively putting her out of the war. She was decommissioned in 1947 and broken up in 1959.

SPECIFICATIONS

MARYLAND

Type: **Battleship**	Armour (deck): **88.9mm (3.5in)**
Length: **190.34m (624.5ft)**	Armour (turrets): **457.2mm (18in)**
Beam: **29.71m (97.5ft)**	Guns: **8x16in; 12x5in; 4x3in**
Draught: **10.69m (35.1ft)**	AA guns: **8x.5in**
Displacement (normal): **33,020tnes (32,500t)**	Aircraft: **None**
Displacement (full load): **38,100tnes (37,500t)**	Crew: **1500**
Machinery: **Geared Turbines**	Launched: **March 1920**
Armour (belt): **342.9m (13.5in)**	Speed: **21 knots**

MISSOURI

SPECIFICATIONS

MISSOURI

Type: **Battleship**	*Armour (deck):* **127mm (5in)**
Length: **270.35m (887ft)**	*Armour (turrets):* **431.8mm (17in)**
Beam: **32.91m (108ft)**	*Guns:* **9x16in; 20x5in**
Draught: **11.27m (37ft)**	*AA guns:* **80x40mm; 60x20mm**
Displacement (normal): **45,720tnes (45,000t)**	*Aircraft:* **Three**
Displacement (full load): **60,280tnes (59,331t)**	*Crew:* **1851**
Machinery: **Geared Turbines**	*Launched:* **January 1944**
Armour (belt): **309.88mm (12.2in)**	*Speed:* **33 knots**

The USS *Missouri* (BB-63) was one of six "Iowa"-class battleships, two of which (*Illinois* and *Kentucky*) were not completed. They were the fastest battleships ever built, with a high length to beam ratio. *Missouri* was launched on 29 January 1944 and completed in June of that year. She joined the Pacific Fleet in time to take part in the first major carrier air raids on the Japanese mainland in March 1945, forming part of the escort force. In many ways these ships were the ultimate in battleship design, but were obsolete even before they left the shipyard.

On 24 March, together with the battleships *Wisconsin* and *New Jersey*, she shelled the island of Okinawa as part of the softening-up operation prior to the American landing. During the landing phase of the operation, on 11 April 1945, she was damaged by a *kamikaze*, and she received moderate damage in another *kamikaze* attack on 16 April. In July she joined other capital ships in bombarding the Japanese mainland, and on 27 August she was part of the 3rd Fleet, sailing into Sagami Bay to accept the Japanese surrender, which was signed on board. *Missouri* carried out shore bombardment during the Korean War and also during the Gulf War, having been rearmed with cruise missiles. She is now a permanent memorial at Pearl Harbor.

PITTSBURGH

The heavy cruiser USS *Pittsburgh* (CA72), formerly named *Albany*, was launched on 22 February 1944. She was one of 24 planned vessels of the "Baltimore" class, and she went into action with the Pacific Fleet in March 1944, sailing from the anchorage at Ulithi Atoll as part of Admiral Mitscher's Task Force 58 to escort aircraft carriers making an attack on the Japanese Home Islands. During this action she and the cruiser *Santa Fe* rescued 1700 survivors from the aircraft carriers *Wasp* and *Franklin*, both heavily damaged by Japanese bombers (*Franklin* had 724 men killed and 265 injured).

In April 1945 *Pittsburgh* was attached to Task Group 58.2, supporting the landings on Okinawa. On 5 June, together with many other US warships, *Pittsburgh* was badly damaged in a typhoon, having 10.6m (35ft) of her bows torn away. However, her design meant she was able to withstand such damage. And it also gave the class long service life.

After repair *Pittsburgh* was returned to active duty and remained in service for many years after the war, being stricken in 1973. Of the original 24 vessels of the "Baltimore" class laid down, six were cancelled in August 1945 with the end of the war in the Pacific. Some, including *Pittsburgh*, were extensively modernized in the 1960s.

SPECIFICATIONS

PITTSBURGH

Type: **Heavy Cruiser**	Armour (deck): **65mm (2.56mm)**
Length: **205.13m (673ft)**	Armour (turrets): **211.32mm (8.32in)**
Beam: **21.25m (69.75ft)**	Guns: **9x8in; 12x5in**
Draught: **6.55m (21.5ft)**	AA guns: **48x40mm; 26x20mm**
Displacement (normal): **13,838tnes (13,620t)**	Aircraft: **Four**
Displacement (full load): **17,475tnes (17,200t)**	Crew: **1200**
Machinery: **Steam Turbines**	Launched: **February 1944**
Armour (belt): **154.43mm (6.08in)**	Speed: **33 knots**

RANGER

SPECIFICATIONS

RANGER

Type: **Aircraft Carrier**	Armour (deck): **25.4mm (1in)**
Length: **234.39m (769ft)**	Armour (turrets): **N/A**
Beam: **24.44m (80.2ft)**	Guns: **8x5in**
Draught: **5.94m (19.5ft)**	AA guns: **16x1.1in; 16x.5in**
Displacement (normal): **14,732tnes (14,500t)**	Aircraft: **70**
Displacement (full load): **18,288tnes (18,000t)**	Crew: **1788**
Machinery: **Geared Turbines**	Launched: **February 1933**
Armour (belt): **25.4mm (1in)**	Speed: **30.36 knots**

The only large carrier in the Atlantic Fleet, *Ranger* led the task force that provided air superiority during the amphibious invasion of French Morocco on 8 November 1942, launching 496 combat sorties in the three-day operation. Following training in Chesapeake Bay, the carrier underwent overhaul in the Norfolk Navy Yard from 16 December 1942 to 7 February 1943. She next transported 75 P-40-L army aircraft to Africa, arriving at Casablanca on 23 February; then patrolled and trained pilots along the New England coast. Departing Halifax on 11 August, she joined the British Home Fleet at Scapa Flow on 19 August.

Ranger departed Scapa Flow with the Home Fleet on 2 October to attack German shipping in Norwegian waters. Her aircraft severely damaged a German tanker, a small troop transport, four small merchantmen, a freighter and a small coaster. She did not sustain any damage during this period.

Ranger returned to Scapa Flow on 6 October 1943, and patrolled with the British Second Battle Squadron until the end of the year. In 1944 she was used for training and then underwent a major refit. Operating out of San Diego, she continued training air groups and squadrons along the peaceful California coast for the rest of the war.

SARATOGA

The USS *Saratoga* (CV-3), sister ship to the *Lexington*, was originally laid down as a battlecruiser in 1920. She was reordered as an aircraft carrier in July 1922, when she was one-third complete, and launched on 7 April 1925. Completed in 1928, she joined the Pacific Fleet in the following year. At the time of the Japanese attack on Pearl Harbor she was transporting fighters to Wake Island and consequently escaped, but on 11 January 1942 she was torpedoed by the Japanese submarine *I-6* 800km (500 miles) southwest of Oahu. Her damage was not major, though.

After repair, in June 1942, she joined Admiral Fitch's Task Force 11, but in August she was again torpedoed, this time by the *I-26*. After further repairs she subsequently operated off Guadalcanal. She provided valuable air cover for US ships operating in the area, as well as flying sorties against the enemy.

Her battle honours included the Battle of the Eastern Solomons, the Rabaul raids, the Gilbert Islands, Kwajalein and Eniwetok; she also served with the British Eastern Fleet in the Indian Ocean in 1944, her air group participating in attacks on Sabang. On 21 February 1945 she was severely damaged when hit by four *kamikazes*, putting her out of the war. On 25 July 1946, her hulk was destroyed in the atomic tests at Bikini.

SPECIFICATIONS

SARATOGA

Type: **Aircraft Carrier**	Armour (deck): **76.2mm (3in)**
Length: **270.66m (888ft)**	Armour (turrets): **N/A**
Beam: **32.3m (106ft)**	Guns: **8x8in; 18x5in; 12x5in**
Draught: **7.34m (24.1ft)**	AA guns: **16x1.1in; 30x20mm**
Displacement (normal): **33,528tnes (33,000t)**	Aircraft: **80–90**
Displacement (full load): **44,094tnes (43,400t)**	Crew: **1890**
Machinery: **Electric Turbines**	Launched: **April 1925**
Armour (belt): **152.4mm (6in)**	Speed: **33 knots**

SOUTH DAKOTA

SPECIFICATIONS

SOUTH DAKOTA

Type: **Battleship**	Armour (deck): **38.1mm (1.5in)**
Length: **207.26m (680ft)**	Armour (turrets): **457.2mm (18in)**
Beam: **32.91m (108ft)**	Guns: **9x16in; 20x5in**
Draught: **11.06m (36.3ft)**	AA guns: **24x40mm; 35x20mm**
Displacement (normal): **35,116tnes (34,563t)**	Aircraft: **None**
Displacement (full load): **46,957tnes (46,218t)**	Crew: **1793**
Machinery: **Geared Turbines**	Launched: **June 1941**
Armour (belt): **309.88mm (12.2in)**	Speed: **27.8 knots**

The USS *South Dakota* (BB-57) – the largest of the four vessels in the above potograph – was leader of a class of four battleships, the others being *Alabama*, *Indiana* and *Massachusetts*. Built at the New York Shipyard, she was launched on 7 June 1941 and completed in March the following year. She was one of the great US battleships of the war.

In September 1942 she suffered hull damage when she struck an uncharted rock in the Tonga Islands, but was repaired in time to see action at the Battle of Santa Cruz, being damaged by a bomb hit in 'A' turret on 26 October. A week later she suffered further damage in a collision with the destroyer *Mahan*, and was again damaged by gunfire on 15 November at the Battle of Guadalcanal, suffering 38 dead.

After this somewhat unfortunate start she went on to acquire an impressive number of battle honours in the Pacific War, taking part in all the US Navy's major operations. She suffered two further mishaps, being hit by a bomb off Saipan on 19 June 1944 with the loss of 27 members of her crew, and damaged by a powder explosion in one of her gun turrets on 6 May 1945. She was present at the Japanese surrender in Sagami Bay on 2 September. *South Dakota* was decommissioned in January 1947 and broken up in 1962.

TEXAS

The USS *Texas* (BB-35) was a Dreadnought-type battleship of the "New York" class, laid down in 1911. She was launched on 18 May 1912 and completed in March 1914. During World War I she was attached to the Royal Navy's Grand Fleet for convoy protection duty in the North Atlantic, operating from Scapa Flow naval base in the Orkneys, and while she was in British waters she became the first US battleship to be fitted with a flying-off platform for spotter aircraft.

From 1919 to 1925 she served with the Pacific Fleet, rejoining the Atlantic Fleet in 1927 after undergoing a period of reconstruction. During World War II, by which time she was obsolete, she again served on convoy protection duty in the Atlantic, and provided fire support for the landings in North Africa in November 1942 and for the D-Day landings in Normandy, June 1944.

During the latter operations, she was damaged by gunfire from a shore battery at Cherbourg. After supporting the Allied landings in the south of France in August 1944 she was transferred to the Pacific, where she provided gunfire support for the American landings on the islands of Iwo Jima and Okinawa. *Texas* was stricken in April 1948 and preserved as a memorial at Galveston, Texas.

SPECIFICATIONS

TEXAS

Type: **Dreadnought**	Armour (deck): **63.5mm (2.5in)**
Length: **174.65m (573ft)**	Armour (turrets): **355.6mm (14in)**
Beam: **29.62m (97.2ft)**	Guns: **10x14in; 37x5in**
Draught: **9.6m (31.5ft)**	AA guns: **8x3in; 8x.5in**
Displacement (normal): **24,432tnes (27,000t)**	Aircraft: **None**
Displacement (full load): **28,956tnes (28,500t)**	Crew: **1054**
Machinery: **Boilers**	Launched: **May 1912**
Armour (belt): **304.8mm (12in)**	Speed: **21 knots**

TUSCALOOSA

SPECIFICATIONS

TUSCALOOSA

Type: **Heavy Cruiser**	Armour (deck): **127mm (5in)**
Length: **179.22m (588ft)**	Armour (turrets): **152.4mm (6in)**
Beam: **18.66m (61.25ft)**	Guns: **9x8in; 8x5in**
Draught: **7.01m (23ft)**	AA guns: **16x40mm; 19x20mm**
Displacement (normal): **10,109tnes (9950t)**	Aircraft: **Four**
Displacement (full load): **13,411tnes (13,200t)**	Crew: **876**
Machinery: **Geared Turbines**	Launched: **November 1933**
Armour (belt): **127mm (5in)**	Speed: **30 knots**

A "New Orleans"-class heavy cruiser, the USS *Tuscaloosa* (CA37) was launched on 15 November 1933. In the early months of World War II she took part in the US patrols in the Atlantic, ranging from Bermuda to the Denmark Strait, and from November 1941 she joined with heavy units of the Royal Navy to counter the expected breakout of the German battleship *Tirpitz* into the North Atlantic (which in the event never happened). In the summer of 1942 she escorted Arctic convoys to Russia, and in November she was one of the warships covering the Allied landings in North Africa, which were relatively easy.

In October 1943 she formed part of an Anglo-American naval force that landed Norwegian troops on the island of Spitzbergen, and later took part in raids on the Norwegian coast.

During the Normandy landings she supported the assault on "Utah" Beach, and in August covered the landings on the French Riviera. At the end of 1944 she was transferred to the Pacific Theatre, where she lent fire support to the American landings on Iwo Jima and Okinawa. *Tuscaloosa* was scrapped at Baltimore in 1959. Three of this class, *Astoria*, *Quincy* and *Vincennes*, were sunk in a cruiser battle off Guadalcanal on 9 August 1942.

YORKTOWN

The aircraft carrier USS *Yorktown* (CV-5) was launched on 4 April 1936 and completed in September of the following year. Her early service was with the Pacific Fleet, but in June 1941 she was transferred to the Atlantic for convoy protection duty. Her stay in this theatre of war was relatively short-lived, as she returned to the Pacific to form the nucleus of Task Force 17 in time to take part in raids on Japanese-held islands in the Central Pacific in January-February 1942. She was one of the greatest aircraft carriers of the war.

In March her air group was in action against Japanese forces landing in New Guinea, and in May she saw action at the Battle of the Coral Sea, being damaged by enemy bombs. She returned to Pearl Harbor, where repairs were made in only 48 hours, and on 28 May she sailed to intercept Japanese naval forces approaching Midway Island. During the ensuing battle, although her torpedo squadrons suffered heavily, her dive-bomber units contributed to the destruction of three Japanese aircraft carriers and therefore helped to tilt the war in the Pacific in the Americans' favour. However, aircraft from the carrier *Hiryu* hit *Yorktown* with two torpedoes and three bombs on 5 June 1942. Desperate attempts were made to save her, but she was sunk by the submarine *I-168* two days later.

SPECIFICATIONS

YORKTOWN

Type: **Aircraft Carrier**	Armour (deck): **None**
Length: **246.73m (809.5ft)**	Armour (turrets): **N/A**
Beam: **25.4m (83.34ft)**	Guns: **8x5in**
Draught: **6.52m (21.4ft)**	AA guns: **16x1.1in; 24x.5in**
Displacement (normal): **20,218tnes (19,900t)**	Aircraft: **100**
Displacement (full load): **25,892tnes (25,484t)**	Crew: **2702**
Machinery: **Geared Turbines**	Launched: **April 1936**
Armour (belt): **101.6mm (4in)**	Speed: **34 knots**

VICKERS MEDIUM

SPECIFICATIONS

VICKERS MEDIUM TANK

Designation:
Vickers Medium Mk IIA

Type:
Medium Tank

Length:
5.36m (17.6ft)

Width:
2.77m (9.1ft)

Height:
2.68m (8.8ft)

Weight:
13,440kg (29,568lb)

Crew:
Five

Main Armament:
3pdr QF

Secondary Armament:
4 x 7.5mm & 2 x .303in

Engine:
Armstrong-Siddeley V-8

Range:
257km (160 miles)

Speed:
24km/h (15mph)

Fording:
.85m (2.78ft)

Trench Crossing:
1.75m (5.75ft)

Armour (hull):
8.25mm (.32in)

Armour (turret):
8.25mm (.32in)

In 1928, Australia purchased four Medium Mk IIA tanks from Great Britain. They differed from the British version by having the coaxial Vickers machine gun on the left of the 3-pounder gun, with a ball-mounted Vickers machine gun on the right. The Vickers Medium tanks were radical for their time, as they were the first tanks with a 360-degree traversing turret to be adopted by the British Army. It is indeed a sign of the rapid development of tank design in the 1930s that they were obsolete by 1939.

The design history of the Vickers is a mystery, as there are no records of correspondence pertaining to it, and no trials reports or memos. However, it was undoubtedly ordered and produced in haste in order to use funds allocated for a new tank by the British Treasury before the financial year ended (the first production models rolled off the factory line in 1923). As well as the fully traversing turret, the Vickers employed a sprung running gear. This was made possible by doing away with the overall track layout of the World War I heavy tanks, and thus lowering the top run of the track. The primary role of the Vickers was one of exploitation – hence its relatively high speed – rather than infantry support. Though obsolete by the outbreak of World War II, it was still used as a training tank.

CHAR B1

The Char B1 was the result of a request for a new French battle tank, and production began in 1935. Though the Char B will forever be associated with the disastrous 1940 campaign and the defeat of the French Army, the tank was in fact of an advanced design.

The specification for the Char B had its origin as far back as 1921, but delays and bureaucratic wrangling meant that the final design was not agreed until 1926. Nevertheless, the result was a good tank. It had self-sealing petrol tanks, a fireproof bulkhead, a gyroscopic compass, an electric starter, lubrication points connected by pipes to grouped lubricators, and a floor escape hatch that was also used for the disposal of empty cases. As steering was through a double differential combined with a hydrostatic unit in the steering drive, lining up the 75mm gun with a target was easy.

The tank ran on a Holt suspension improved by the firm FCM, and was fully covered by skirting. The B1's main problem was the poor distribution of the four-man crew, with the one-man turret being served by the commander, who also had to give orders to the crew, watch his own and enemy units, as well as load and fire the gun. In general with other French tanks, individual crew members felt isolated inside the B1. However, they were relatively well protected by the B1's armour.

SPECIFICATIONS

CHAR B1

Designation:
Char de Bataille B1

Type:
Heavy Tank

Length:
6.37m (20.92ft)

Width:
2.5m (8.11ft)

Height:
2.8m (9.2ft)

Weight:
30,545kg (67,200lb)

Crew:
Four

Main Armament:
1 x 75mm, 1 x 47mm

Secondary Armament:
2 x 7.5mm

Engine:
Renault six-cylinder

Range:
180km (112 miles)

Speed:
27.5km/h (17.mph)

Fording:
Unknown

Trench Crossing:
2.74m (9ft)

Armour (hull):
14mm (.6in)

Armour (turret):
14mm (.6in)

CHAR B1-BIS

SPECIFICATIONS

CHAR B1-BIS

Designation:
Char de Bataille B1-bis

Type:
Heavy Tank

Length:
6.38m (20.94ft)

Width:
2.5m (8.11ft)

Height:
2.79m (9.17ft)

Weight:
32,581m (71,680lb)

Crew:
Four

Main Armament:
1 x 75mm, 1 x 47mm

Secondary Armament:
2 x 7.5mm

Engine:
Renault six-cylinder

Range:
180km (112.5 miles)

Speed:
27.52km/h (17.2mph)

Fording:
Unknown

Trench Crossing:
2.74m (9ft)

Armour (hull):
14mm (.6in)

Armour (turret):
65mm (2.6in)

Based on the Char B1, the B1-bis had armour thickness increased to 65mm (2.6in) and was fitted with a new APX4 turret and gun. The first models were fitted with a 250hp engine, though this was later replaced by a 300hp aircraft motor. In addition, the later production models had a greater range thanks to auxiliary fuel tanks.

The bis was produced from 1937 by Renault, FAMH, Saint-Chamond and Schneider, with AMX also becoming involved in the manufacturing process in 1939. By the time of the German invasion of France in May 1940 some 380 Char Bs had been built, all of them bis models save for 35 of the earlier B1 variants.

The Char B was the main strike force of the four French armoured divisions in 1940, and as such represented the most significant Allied tank during the campaign (its 75mm gun could knock out any German tank then in service). Each division was composed of four battalions of tanks, made up of two battalions of Char B1-bis types and two battalions of light tanks. Those Char B1s that had not been destroyed in the fighting in France were used by the Germans as training vehicles, flamethrowers or for self-propelled mountings. In German service they performed well – testimony to the overall sound design of the vehicle.

CHAR S-35

The S-35 was regarded as the best tank in French service in 1940, and because of its excellent design the Germans pressed many into their own service after the fall of France in 1940. The S-35 had a similar turret design to the Char B1, but was faster with a road speed of 15.62km/h (25mph). Though the hull was rather high, its armour was well-shaped and rounded to deflect shots.

The 47mm main gun and coaxial 7.5mm machine gun were mounted in an electrically traversed turret which was probably better than anything the Germans possessed in 1940. That said, as ever, the turret performance was degraded by the fact that the commander was also the gunner. The tank was powered by a Somua V-8 190hp engine linked to a synchronised five-speed gearbox, which transmitted the drive to the tracks via rear sprockets.

The S-35 comprised one of the principal fighting vehicles of the French mechanised cavalry divisions, with each division having one regiment of S-35s. The tank ran over the nine road wheels each side, all protected by skirting plates. The first armoured fighting vehicle with an all-cast hull and turret construction, a total of 500 S-35s were built. At the time of the invasion of Poland in September 1939, the French Army had 261 S-35s; the rest were provided in response to increased production.

SPECIFICATIONS

CHAR S-35

Designation: **Char de Cavalerie S-35**	Secondary Armament: **1 x 7.5mm**
Type: **Medium Tank**	Engine: **Somua V-8 190hp**
Length: **5.28m (17.33ft)**	Range: **257km (160.6 miles)**
Width: **1.85m (6.06ft)**	Speed: **15.62km/h (25mph)**
Height: **2.6m (8.58ft)**	Fording: **.8m (2.62ft)**
Weight: **20,363kg (44,800lb)**	Trench Crossing: **1.6m (5.25ft)**
Crew: **Three**	Armour (hull): **36mm (1.4in)**
Main Armament: **47mm**	Armour (turret): **55mm (2.16in)**

CHAR LEGER H-38

SPECIFICATIONS

CHAR LEGER H-38

Designation:
Char Léger Hotchkiss H-38

Type:
Light Tank

Length:
4.21m (13.83ft)

Width:
1.95m (6.39in)

Height:
2.13m (7ft)

Weight:
12,218kg (26,880lb)

Crew:
Two

Main Armament:
37mm

Secondary Armament:
1 x 7.5mm

Engine:
Hotchkiss six-cylinder

Range:
150km (93.75 miles)

Speed:
36km/h (22mph)

Fording:
.85m (2.78ft)

Trench Crossing:
1.8m (5.9ft)

Armour (hull):
34mm (1.3in)

Armour (turret):
45mm (1.77in)

Similar to the H-35, the Hotchkiss H-38 had a larger-capacity engine (5976cc) which developed 120hp at 2800rpm. In 1940 the French had 800 H-38s in service, and many were used by the German Army after the fall of France. Some turretless models were used by the artillery as tractors, others became ammunition carriers, and a few were modified to fire rockets to provide artillery support. Steering was controlled by means of a Cleveland differential, with the tracks being driven by front sprockets.

Essentially a cavalry tank, it was produced for the French Army from 1936 onwards. Its one-man APXR 1 turret housed a short-barrelled 37mm gun and a single machine gun. With one extra road wheel each side, the tank had a long track base which gave good cross-country performance at speed.

In German use, H-38s were issued to newly raised units and to units that were reforming in France after suffering heavy losses in Russia. Between 1941 and 1943, units equipped with H-38s were sent to Norway and the Balkans. On 30 December 1944, there were still 29 H-38s in German service. The H-39 variant was fitted with a new engine and a long-barrelled 37mm main gun. It was used by the Germans on the Eastern Front and Mediterranean, and also by Free French forces.

CHAR LEGER R-35

The R-35 was built by Renault as a replacement for its predecessor, the FT-17. A two-man vehicle, it was designed to re-equip the tank regiments supporting infantry divisions. As such it was reasonably well armoured and armed, though its Renault four-cylinder 82hp engine achieved a top speed of only 19.2km/h (12mph) – though this was deemed adequate for its roles of accompanying infantry.

The rear-mounted engine drove sprockets at the front of the track, with the suspension consisting of five road wheels and a low-mounted idler wheel at the rear on each side. The wheels themselves were mounted in two articulated bogies, each of two wheels, while wheel movement was controlled by springs made up of horizontally mounted rubber washers. The R-35 was an important element in the French rearmament programme in the 1930s, and it equipped 23 battalions by the time of the German invasion of France in 1940.

There was an improved model of the R-35 which was equipped with the longer-barrelled SA 38 37mm gun, while the R-40 variant was fitted with an entirely new suspension system designed by AMX, with armoured side skirts. This vehicle had far better cross-country performance that the R-35, but only two battalions had been equipped with it by 1940.

SPECIFICATIONS

CHAR LEGER R-35

Designation: **Char Léger Renault R-35**	*Secondary Armament:* **1 x 7.5mm**
Type: **Light Tank**	*Engine:* **Renault four-cylinder**
Length: **4m (13.16ft)**	*Range:* **140km (87.5 miles)**
Width: **1.85m (6.06ft)**	*Speed:* **19.2km/h (12mph)**
Height: **2.08m (6.83ft)**	*Fording:* **.8m (2.62ft)**
Weight: **10,181kg (22,400lb)**	*Trench Crossing:* **1.6m (5.25ft)**
Crew: **Two**	*Armour (hull):* **32mm (1.25in)**
Main Armament: **37mm**	*Armour (turret):* **45mm (1.77in)**

RENAULT FT

SPECIFICATIONS

RENAULT FT

Designation:
Renault FT

Type:
Light Tank

Length:
4m (13.25ft)

Width:
1.71m (5.61ft)

Height:
2.13m (7ft)

Weight:
6618kg (14,560lb)

Crew:
Two

Main Armament:
1 x 7.5mm/37mm gun

Secondary Armament:
None

Engine:
Renault four-cylinder

Range:
35.4km (22 miles)

Speed:
7.68km/h (4.8mph)

Fording:
.9m (3ft)

Trench Crossing:
1.8m (5.9ft)

Armour (hull):
16mm (.63in)

Armour (turret):
22mm (.86in)

The FT series of tanks was originally conceived as a light tank to accompany infantry units on the battlefield in World War I. The first time it was used in battle was on 31 May 1918 in the Forest of Retz. Suspension consisted of leaf springs combined with a vertical coil which tensioned the upper track run. Its front idlers were of the steel-rimmed laminated wood type.

During the 1930s the FT (on the right in the above photograph) series was still in service, though by this time the new 7.5mm Model 31 machine gun had superseded the 8mm Hotchkiss variant. The FT-17 variant of the tank was equipped with the 37mm Puteaux gun, with production of this model totalling 1830. In 1939 the French still had 1600 FTs in their army.

Both cannon- and machine gun-armed Renault FTs were supplied to Belgium, Brazil, Canada, China, Czechoslovakia, Finland, Holland, Japan, Poland, Spain and the United States. After the fall of France in June 1940, the Germans used many FT tanks for internal security duties. In addition, some FT turrets were incorporated as observation cupolas into the Atlantic Wall defences. A version which was armed with a short-barrelled 75mm gun was called the Renault BS. Only a few were built, but some were encountered in Axis service in North Africa by the Allies.

BRUMMBÄR

The Sturmpanzer IV (Brummbär) carried the 150mm StuH43 gun on a standard Panzer IV chassis. It was developed by Alkett, who designed the superstructure, while Krupp redesigned the Panzer IV chassis. Hitler, thinking they could be more potent than the StuG III, ordered the Brummbär into production at the end of 1942. Initial production began in April 1943, with a first batch of 60 being completed by May (this series had an armour plate 50mm [1.96in] thick bolted on to the basic 50mm- [1.96in-] thick hull front).

These vehicles had sliding-shutter visors for the driver, similar to those mounted on the Tiger I. However, in the later vehicles the driver was provided with a periscope. Full-scale production began in November 1943 and continued until the end of World War II. By that time 298 had been built. The final version of the vehicle had a redesigned superstructure which incorporated a ball-mounted machine gun in the top left-hand corner of the front plate, plus a cupola for the commander.

The first Brummbärs were issued to Sturmpanzer Abteilung 216 just prior to the Kursk Offensive in July 1943. A further three Sturmpanzer Abteilungs were raised (217, 218 and 219), and all of them saw service on the Eastern Front, as well as in the West and Italy.

SPECIFICATIONS

BRUMMBÄR

Designation: **StuG IV 15cm StuH43**	Secondary Armament: **2 x 7.92mm**
Type: **Assault Infantry Gun**	Engine: **Maybach HL120TRM**
Length: **5.93m (19.45ft)**	Range: **210km (131 miles)**
Width: **2.88m (9.44ft)**	Speed: **40km/h (28.12mph)**
Height: **2.52m (8.26ft)**	Fording: **1m (3.25ft)**
Weight: **28,712kg (63,168lb)**	Trench Crossing: **2.2m (7.25ft)**
Crew: **Five**	Armour (hull): **80mm (3.14in)**
Main Armament: **150mm**	Armour (turret): **100mm (3.93in)**

GRILLE

SPECIFICATIONS

GRILLE

Designation:
SdKfz 138/1

Secondary Armament:
1 x 7.92mm

Type:
SP Heavy Infantry Gun

Engine:
Praga EPA/2

Length:
4.61m (14ft)

Range:
185km (115.6 miles)

Width:
2.16m (7.08ft)

Speed:
35km/h (21.87mph)

Height:
2.4m (7.87ft)

Fording:
.9m (3ft)

Weight:
11,709kg (25,760lb)

Trench Crossing:
1.87m (6.13ft)

Crew:
Five

Armour (hull):
50mm (1.96in)

Main Armament:
150mm

Armour (turret):
25mm (.98in)

The Grille was first ordered for construction on the new self-propelled gun chassis that BMM was developing, the resultant vehicle being designated Sf 38(t) Ausf K. However, wartime demands resulted in Panzer 38(t)s being used instead, being converted by BMM as they returned from the front for refits. The standard chassis was fitted with a new fighting compartment superstructure, which had to be extended over the engine compartment in order to accommodate the sIG33/1 L/12 heavy gun and its 15 rounds of ammunition.

A total of 90 were produced between February and April 1943. All Grilles were issued to the heavy infantry assault gun companies of panzergrenadier regiments, serving in Russia, Tunisia, Italy and France from early 1943. In June 1944, at the time of the D-Day landings, the Grille was still in service with the 38th Panzer Heavy Infantry Assault Gun Abteilung of the 2nd Panzer Division in Normandy.

The Praga EPA/2 engine had five forward gears and one reverse, and gave a top speed of 35km/h (21.87mph). As with most infantry assault guns, the crew were housed in an open superstructure, though the provision of an MG34 machine gun gave them some protection from enemy infantry antitank squads.

HUMMEL

The Hummel was an attempt to provide armoured units with artillery support on a fully tracked armoured chassis. The 150mm sFH18/1L/30 gun was mounted on a Panzer IV chassis, though this was only intended as an interim measure until a chassis designed specifically for self-propelled gun platforms could be developed and produced. To accommodate the gun, the engine was moved forward to a central position, while the Hummel's drive sprocket was of the type designed for the Panzer III. The open-topped fighting compartment was enclosed on all four sides by slanted armour plates bolted to the hull, while the glacis plate was extended and there was a small compartment for the driver on the left-hand side.

The gun was mounted over the engine, which gave the Hummel a high silhouette. The specially designed ammunition carriers acted as supply vehicles for the Hummels, and 157 were built in total.

The Hummel was issued to the panzer divisions, where they served in the heavy batteries of the armoured artillery detachments. At first each panzer division was equipped with six Hummels in a single heavy battery, though later a second heavy battery was added. They fought at Kursk in mid-1943, and continued in service until the end of the war in May 1945.

SPECIFICATIONS

HUMMEL

Designation:
SdKfz 165

Type:
SP Heavy Howitzer

Length:
7.17m (23.52ft)

Width:
2.87m (9.41ft)

Height:
2.81m (9.23ft)

Weight:
24,436kg (53,760lb)

Crew:
Five

Main Armament:
150mm

Secondary Armament:
1 x 7.92mm

Engine:
HL 120TRM

Range:
215km (134.4 miles)

Speed:
42km/h (26.25mph)

Fording:
.99m (3.25ft)

Trench Crossing:
2.2m (7.25ft)

Armour (hull):
30mm (1.18in)

Armour (turret):
10mm (.39in)

JAGDPANTHER

SPECIFICATIONS

JAGDPANTHER

Designation:
SdKfz 173

Type:
Heavy Tank Destroyer

Length:
9.9m (32.8ft)

Width:
3.27m (10.72ft)

Height:
2.72m (8.92ft)

Weight:
46,836kg (103,040lb)

Crew:
Five

Main Armament:
88mm

Secondary Armament:
1 x 7.92mm

Engine:
Maybach HL230P30

Range:
160km (100 miles)

Speed:
46km/h (28.75mph)

Fording:
1.7m (5.57ft)

Trench Crossing:
1.9m (6.23ft)

Armour (hull):
60mm (2.36in)

Armour (turret):
80mm (3.14in)

An order to develop a heavy assault gun by mating the 88mm Pak L/71 gun to a Panther chassis was given on 2 October 1942, and a wooden mock-up was completed by October 1943. Hitler saw the prototype on 16 December 1943, and production began in January 1944.

The upper hull plates and side plates of the standard Panther chassis were extended to create the fighting compartment. The 88mm Pak 43/3 gun was installed in a gun mount in the sloping front plate (early production vehicles had the gun mount welded to the superstructure front plate). Later production models had a gun mount which was protruded and was bolted in place. Defence against enemy infantry was provided by a *Hahverteidigungsgerät* (close-defence weapon) mounted in the superstructure roof, plus a machine gun in a hull mount in the superstructure front.

The Jagdpanther was one of the finest tank destroyers of the war. The first vehicles were issued to the 559th and 654th Anti-Tank Battalions, though only the 654th received the full complement of 42 vehicles. The largest assembly of Jagdpanthers in the war took place during the Ardennes Offensive in December 1944. Thereafter they were also issued to the tank detachments of at least seven panzer divisions. In total, 392 were produced between January 1944 and March 1945.

MARDER II

The Marder II antitank vehicle was essentially a 75mm Pak 40/2 gun mated to a Panzer II chassis. By May 1942 the combat effectiveness of the Panzer II (still being produced at a rate of 50 per month) was being questioned – it was certainly obsolete by this date. As a result, early in June it was decided that half the production would be given to mounting the Pak 40 gun on the Panzer II chassis, though assembly was cut short in June 1943 to concentrate on production of the Wespe (see page 42).

The hull and superstructure front of the Marder II remained the same as the standard Panzer II Ausf F. A further superstructure was built to create the fighting compartment, with the upper half of the field-carriage mount for the Pak 40 being retained. However, girders were added to provide support for the gun. Secondary armament for the three-man crew was provided by one 7.92mm MG 34 machine gun, while 37 rounds were carried for the main gun.

A total of 576 Marder IIs were built between June 1942 and June 1943, with a further 75 Panzer IIs being converted between July 1943 and March 1944. The vehicles were issued to antitank detachments from July 1942 onwards, and served in both the East and West until the end of the war.

SPECIFICATIONS

MARDER II

Designation: SdKfz 131	**Secondary Armament:** 1 x 7.92mm
Type: SP Antitank Gun	**Engine:** Maybach HL62TRM
Length: 6.36m (20.86ft)	**Range:** 190km (118.7 miles)
Width: 2.28m (7.48ft)	**Speed:** 40km/h (25mph)
Height: 2.2m (7.21ft)	**Fording:** .85m (2.78ft)
Weight: 10,996kg (24,192lb)	**Trench Crossing:** 1.75m (5.74ft)
Crew: Three	**Armour (hull):** 35mm (1.37in)
Main Armament: 75mm	**Armour (superstructure):** 30mm (1.18in)

MARDER III

SPECIFICATIONS

MARDER III

Designation:
SdKfz 138

Type:
SP Antitank Gun

Length:
4.95m (16.24ft)

Width:
2.15m (7.05ft)

Height:
2.48m (8.13ft)

Weight:
10,691kg (23,520lb)

Crew:
Four

Main Armament:
75mm

Secondary Armament:
1 x 7.92mm

Engine:
Praga AC

Range:
190km (118.75 miles)

Speed:
42km/h (26.25mph)

Fording:
.9m (3ft)

Trench Crossing:
1.87m (6.13ft)

Armour (hull):
20mm (.78in)

Armour (superstructure):
10mm (.39in)

On orders from Hitler, in July 1942 production capacity of the Panzer 38(t) was switched to self-propelled gun chassis. This prompted a new design in which the engine was moved to the centre of the vehicle, which allowed the gun to be moved to the rear. In addition, frontal armour was reduced, which also lessened overall weight.

The vehicle mounted the the potent 75mm Pak 40/3 gun, and at the beginning of February 1943 Hitler was informed that production would reach 150 units per month (though this level was not reached until November of that year). In May 1944, production of the Marder III was terminated in favour of the Jagdpanzer Hetzer. By that time a total of 975 vehicles had been produced for the army.

Those Marders built during 1943 had a rounded, cast cover for the driving compartment at the front right-hand side of the vehicle. At the end of 1943, a simpler welded cover was introduced, with the front towing tugs formed from extensions of the side armour plate.

The Marder III was deployed to the antitank detachments of both panzer and infantry divisions from May 1943. They served on all fronts during the war, especially on the Eastern Front, and at the end of the war there were still over 300 in Wehrmacht service.

NASHORN

The Nashorn (Rhinoceros), later called Hornisse (Hornet), was designed to accommodate the 88mm Pak 43/1 L/71 gun – the most powerful tank armament produced by the Germans in World War II, and the most effective anti-armour gun built by either side. With a muzzle velocity of 1018m/sec (3340ft/sec), it could destroy any Allied tank in service up to the end of the war in Europe in May 1945.

In October 1942, it was decided to use 100 vehicles for the summer offensive on the Eastern Front from the initial order of 500. As with the Hummel (see page 15), the chassis used a lengthened Panzer IV hull with the motor moved forward to a central position.

Some 494 Nashorns were delivered between February 1943 and March 1945, and they were assigned to heavy antitank units which acted as independent formations attached to corps or armies. As such, they became highly effective mobile tank-hunting squads, especially on the Eastern Front, where they knocked out hundreds of Soviet T-34s. The first Wehrmacht unit to be equipped with Nashorns was the 655th Heavy Anti-Tank Battalion (schwere Panzerjägerabteilung) on the Eastern Front in the summer of 1943. In total, five other heavy tank-hunter units were formed, seeing service in Italy, the West and Russia.

SPECIFICATIONS

NASHORN

Designation: **SdKfz 164**	*Secondary Armament:* **1 x 7.92mm**
Type: **SP Heavy Antitank Gun**	*Engine:* **Maybach HL120TRM**
Length: **8.44m (27.69ft)**	*Range:* **190km (118.7 miles)**
Width: **2.86m (9.38ft)**	*Speed:* **215km (134.37 miles)**
Height: **2.65m (8.69ft)**	*Fording:* **.8m (2.62ft)**
Weight: **24,436kg (53,760lb)**	*Trench Crossing:* **2.3m (7.54ft)**
Crew: **Four**	*Armour (hull):* **30mm (1.18in)**
Main Armament: **88mm**	*Armour (superstructure):* **10mm (.39in)**

PAK 40 (SF)

SPECIFICATIONS

PAK 40 (SF)

Designation: **Geschützwagen 39H(f)**	Secondary Armament: **1 x 7.92mm**
Type: **SP Antitank Gun**	Engine: **Hotchkiss Six-cylinder**
Length: **5.31m (17.42ft)**	Range: **150km (93.75 miles)**
Width: **1.83m (6ft)**	Speed: **36km/h (22.5mph)**
Height: **2.23m (7.31ft)**	Fording: **.8m (2.62ft)**
Weight: **8644kg (19,017lb)**	Trench Crossing: **1.6m (5.25ft)**
Crew: **Four**	Armour (hull): **30mm (1.18in)**
Main Armament: **75mm**	Armour (superstructure): **30mm (1.18in)**

With the capture of so many vehicles following the fall of France in June 1940, the Germans set about converting them for their own use. This was not an immediate decision, as the army was flushed with victory and few believed that large numbers of non-German armoured fighting vehicles would be needed. It was only with the huge losses experienced on the Eastern Front, plus the appearance of the Soviet T-34, that prompted the necessity for large numbers of antitank platforms. One such vehicle was the PaK40 (SF), a self-propelled antitank gun on a light tank chassis. The conversion was unusual in that the engine was left in the rear.

The superstructure and engine cover were removed and a new plate for the driver was fitted as part of the new self-propelled gun conversion. The numbers converted were not great: a total of 24 were modified to carry the 75mm gun (this model is shown in the above photograph), while a further 48 were modified to mount the larger 105mm gun. In both models the gun had a traverse of 30 degrees to the left and right, with an elevation of plus 22 degrees to minus five degrees.

These self-propelled armoured fighting vehicles were assigned to the 8th Panzerartillerie Abteilung serving in France, and they saw action following the Allied D-Day landings in June 1944.

PANZER I

In the early 1930s the German Army needed a tank that could be built cheaply and in large numbers for training purposes. The Krupp design (the L.K.A.1) was selected as the first production model in 1934, eventually becoming the Panzer IA. The earliest versions had open-top hulls, no turrets and were designated as agricultural tractors to disguise their true purpose.

The layout comprised a rear-mounted engine with the transmission led forward to front-driving sprockets. The crew compartment was in the centre of the vehicle, with the driver on the left. The turret, armed with two machine guns, was off-set to the right on the roof of the hull. Suspension consisted of independently sprung front road wheels with the remaining wheels in pairs on leaf springs linked by a girder for extra rigidity.

Production of the Panzer IA ran to 500 vehicles, with nearly 2000 of the B variant being produced. In 1936 both types were battle-tested during the Spanish Civil War. It was soon discovered that the absence of an antitank gun and the two-man turret were major disadvantages. By 1939, insufficient numbers of the more powerful Panzer II and Panzer III had been built, and so the Panzer I saw service in Poland in 1939 and France in 1940. Despite its obsolescence, a few Panzer Is saw service during the invasion of Russia in 1941.

SPECIFICATIONS

PANZER I

Designation:
Sdkfz 101

Type:
Light Tank

Length:
4.02m (13.18ft)

Width:
2.06m (6.75ft)

Height:
1.72m (5.64ft)

Weight:
5498kg (12,096lb)

Crew:
Two

Main Armament:
2 x 7.92mm

Secondary Armament:
None

Engine:
Krupp M305

Range:
145km (90.62 miles)

Speed:
37km/h (23.12mph)

Fording:
.85m (2.78ft)

Trench Crossing:
1.75m (5.74ft)

Armour (hull):
13mm (.51in)

Armour (turret):
13mm (.51in)

PANZER II

SPECIFICATIONS

PANZER II

Designation:
SdKfz 121

Secondary Armament:
1 x 7.92mm

Type:
Light Tank

Engine:
Maybach HL62TR

Length:
4.81m (15.78ft)

Range:
200km (125 miles)

Width:
2.3m (7.5ft)

Speed:
40km/h (25mph)

Height:
1.99m (6.52ft)

Fording:
.85m (2.78ft)

Weight:
9061kg (19,936lb)

Trench Crossing:
1.75m (5.74ft)

Crew:
Three

Armour (hull):
14.5mm (.57in)

Main Armament:
20mm

Armour (turret):
14.5mm (.57in)

Designed by the company MAN, the Panzer II fulfilled a light tank requirement for the German Army. The first 25 pre-production machines were built in 1935, the basic design having a rear engine and front drive. During the initial stages the tank underwent a number of minor changes, such as turret modifications and work on the front superstructure. The main production versions were the Ausf B and C models, which had an angled nose, and splash plates on the top and bottom of the mantlet.

The Ausf D and E models were produced by Daimler-Benz in 1939, and incorporated a Famo/Christie-type suspension to give a top speed of 56km/h (35mph). However, cross-country performance was poor and these particular models were withdrawn from service early. The Ausf F, G and J models were improved versions of the Ausf C, which were up-armoured to give protection from heavier antitank guns. This meant 35mm (1.37in) of frontal armour and 20mm (.78in) of side armour.

The Ausf A–C models were widely used in the early period of World War II, especially in Poland in 1939 and France in 1940. At the beginning of the attack in the West in May 1940, for example, there were 965 Panzer IIs in German service – forming the backbone of the 2500 German tanks used in the campaign.

PANZER III AUSF F

During the 1930s, it was envisaged that the core of the German panzer divisions would be a medium tank armed with a 37mm or 50mm armour-piercing gun. A number of prototype vehicles were built by Daimler-Benz, Rheinmetall, MAN and Krupp in response to this requirement. Tested in 1936–37, the Daimler-Benz model was chosen for further development.

The early models – Ausf A, B, C and D – had different forms of suspension, ranging from five large road wheels on coil springs per side (on the Ausf A) to eight small wheels on leaf springs (on the Ausf B, C and D). The turret and hull were essentially the same in all models. In the Ausf E version the suspension consisted of six road wheels each side on a transverse torsion-bar system, and this arrangement would continue through the rest of the Panzer III's production life.

The Ausf F was similar to the Ausf E, the main difference being to the ignition system, with cast air intakes being added to the upper hull plate to allow air circulation for brakes and final-drive cooling. Most were armed with the 37mm KwK L/46.5 gun, but around 100 were equipped with the 50mm KwK L42 model. Between August 1940 and 1942, many of the those remaining were up-gunned to 50mm calibre, with more armour also being added to the hull and superstructure.

SPECIFICATIONS

PANZER III AUSF F

Designation:
SdKfz 141

Type:
Medium Tank

Length:
5.38m (17.65ft)

Width:
2.95m (9.67ft)

Height:
2.44m (8ft)

Weight:
20,160kg (44,352lb)

Crew:
Five

Main Armament:
37mm

Secondary Armament:
2 x 7.92mm

Engine:
Maybach HL120TRM

Range:
165km (101 miles)

Speed:
40km/h (25mph)

Fording:
.8m (2.62ft)

Trench Crossing:
2.59m (8.5ft)

Armour (hull):
30mm (1.18in)

Armour (turret):
30mm (1.18in)

PANZER III AUSF J

SPECIFICATIONS

PANZER III AUSF J

Designation: SdKfz 141	**Secondary Armament:** 2 x 7.92mm
Type: Medium Tank	**Engine:** Maybach HL120TRM
Length: 5.52m (18.11ft)	**Range:** 155km (96.8 miles)
Width: 2.95m (9.67ft)	**Speed:** 40km/h (25mph)
Height: 2.5m (8.2ft)	**Fording:** .8m (2.62ft)
Weight: 21,890kg (48,160lb)	**Trench Crossing:** 2.59m (8.5ft)
Crew: Five	**Armour (hull):** 30mm (1.18in)
Main Armament: 50mm	**Armour (turret):** 50mm (1.96in)

The Panzer III Ausf J was the first variant of the tank to be built to have the armour protection increased to a basic 50mm (1.96in). The armour change required new fittings. In addition, an improved driver's visor was fitted, plus a new ball-shaped hull machine-gun mount. The upper hull front accommodated newly designed air intakes for brakes and final-drive cooling, while single-piece access hatches in the glacis were fitted in place of the double hatch.

The initial order for the Ausf J was for 900, but this was later increased to 2700. The new vehicle, with its 50mm KwK L/42 gun, was used to equip the 2nd and 5th Panzer Divisions, plus an independent panzer regiment. These units were sent to the Eastern Front in September 1941, where they took part in the later stages of Operation Barbarossa, the German invasion of the Soviet Union, suffering many losses (their engines and suspension systems suffered in the freezing conditions).

The rest of the Ausf Js were used as replacement vehicles for the 1400 Panzers II tanks lost during the first year of fighting in Russia and North Africa. Though the Panzer III was outclassed by the T-34 in the East from the end of 1941, there were still 500 KwK L/42-armed Panzer IIIs in service at the beginning of the German summer offensive in mid-1943.

PANZER III AUSF N

The Panzer III Ausf N was an attempt to increase the potency of the tank by arming it with the 75mm KwK L/24 gun. This weapon fired an effective high-explosive round and an excellent shaped-charge that had better penetration than the long-barrelled KwK39 L/60 which it replaced.

The initial order was for 450 tanks, but the troops at the front liked the Ausf N so much that Ausf M models were also equipped with the short-barrelled 75mm gun. With additional Panzer IIIs being so armed, the total number of Ausf Ns was brought up to 700.

The Ausf N was recognisable by its short-barrelled gun and the lack of spaced armour on the mantlet. Many of the later Ausf Ns were fitted with a new cupola with thicker armour and a single hatch in place of the earlier split-hatch design. Ausf Ns were also given side skirts for greater protection from March 1943.

In the field the Ausf N was used to provide close support for the Tigers (each heavy tank company had 10 Ausf Ns to nine Tigers), as the smaller vehicle was more agile at close quarters, whereas the Tiger was rather slow and vulnerable. The Ausf N was also used in the panzer regiments of the panzer divisions. In mid-1943, during the Kursk Offensive, German panzer units were equipped with 155 Panzer III Ausf Ns.

SPECIFICATIONS

PANZER III AUSF N

Designation:
SdKfz 141/2

Type:
Medium Tank

Length:
5.65m (18.53ft)

Width:
2.95m (9.67ft)

Height:
2.5m (8.2ft)

Weight:
23,418kg (51,520lb)

Crew:
Five

Main Armament:
75mm

Secondary Armament:
2 x 7.92mm

Engine:
Maybach HL120TRM

Range:
155km (96.8 miles)

Speed:
40km/h (25mph)

Fording:
.8m (2.62ft)

Trench Crossing:
2.59m (8.5ft)

Armour (hull):
50mm (1.96in)

Armour (turret):
50mm (1.96in)

PANZER IV AUSF C

SPECIFICATIONS

PANZER IV AUSF C

Designation:
SdKfz 161

Type:
Medium Support Tank

Length:
5.92m (19.42ft)

Width:
3.29m (10.79ft)

Height:
2.68m (8.79ft)

Weight:
19,345kg (42,560lb)

Crew:
Five

Main Armament:
75mm

Secondary Armament:
1 x 7.92mm

Engine:
Maybach HL120TRM

Range:
200km (125 miles)

Speed:
40km/h (25mph)

Fording:
1m (3.25ft)

Trench Crossing:
2.2m (7.25ft)

Armour (hull):
30mm (1.18in)

Armour (turret):
30mm (1.18in)

By far the most enduring of the main types of German tank, the Panzer IV was specified as a medium tank in the 20-ton class, to be armed with a 75mm gun. The order to build the vehicle was awarded to Krupp, who initially proposed interleaved road wheels for suspension. However, the actual suspension used was much more simple: eight road wheels on each side suspended in pairs on leaf springs. Like other German tanks of the period, the Panzer IV's engine was located at the rear with the transmission led forward to the final drive via sprockets at the front of the track.

The Ausf C, which was armed with the KwK 37 l/24 gun, incorporated a number of minor changes to the design of the Ausf B, including improved turret face, a new gun mantlet housing, an altered motor mount, and an armoured sleeve that protected the coaxial machine gun. Later, to extend combat life, additional armour plates were bolted to the hull and superstructure sides.

An initial order for the Ausf C was for 300 vehicles, but only 134 were completed. Production took place between September 1938 and August 1939, and the Ausf C saw service in Poland in 1939 and the West in the summer of 1940. The vehicle remained in service until 1943, but by then numbers had dwindled drastically due to battlefield attrition.

PANZER IV AUSF H

Between April 1943 and July 1944, a total of 3774 Panzer IV Ausf Hs were produced. The basic difference between this model and the Ausf G variant was the fitting of the SSG77 transmission. In addition, armour thickness was increased to 80mm (3.14in) from 50mm (1.96in). A host of other minor modifications included external air filters, all-steel rollers, a cupola mount for an antiaircraft machine gun, a new idler, the deletion of side vision ports for the driver and radio operator, and a new cupola with thicker armour.

Main armament consisted of the 75mm KwK40 L/48 gun. The Ausf H and J models were up-gunned with this weapon in 1943–44. It was an excellent all-round gun, which fired a potent high-explosive round and also had a good anti-armour performance. This was especially true at short ranges when using the PzGr40 armour-piercing, composite non-rigid round.

Following the introduction into service of the Panther, all panzer regiments in a panzer division were to have one detachment of Panthers and one detachment of Panzer IVs. However, because of problems with the Panther, panzer divisions had a second detachment of Panzer IVs. In France in June 1944, for example, most of the 748 Panzer IVs with the nine German panzer divisions were Ausf H models.

SPECIFICATIONS

PANZER IV AUSF H

Designation: **SdKfz 161/2**	Secondary Armament: **1 x 7.92mm**
Type: **Medium Tank**	Engine: **Maybach HL120TRM**
Length: **7.02m (23.03ft)**	Range: **210km (131 miles)**
Width: **3.29m (10.79ft)**	Speed: **38km/h (23.75mph)**
Height: **2.68m (8.79ft)**	Fording: **1m (3.25ft)**
Weight: **25,454kg (56,000lb)**	Trench Crossing: **2.2m (7.25ft)**
Crew: **Five**	Armour (hull): **80mm (3.14in)**
Main Armament: **75mm**	Armour (turret): **50mm (1.96in)**

PANZER V AUSF D

SPECIFICATIONS

PANZER V AUSF D

Designation:
SdKfz 171

Secondary Armament:
2 x 7.92mm

Type:
Heavy Medium Tank

Engine:
Maybach HL 230P30

Length:
8.86m (29.06ft)

Range:
200km (125 miles)

Width:
3.43m (11.25ft)

Speed:
46km/h (28.75 miles)

Height:
2.95m (9.67ft)

Fording:
1.7m (5.57ft)

Weight:
43,781kg (96,320lb)

Trench Crossing:
1.91m (6.26ft)

Crew:
Five

Armour (hull):
80mm (3.14in)

Main Armament:
75mm

Armour (turret):
100mm (3.93in)

After the shock of encountering the T-34 in late 1941, Hitler ordered the development of a similar tank in the 30-ton class. He ordered the MAN design into production on 14 May 1942, with factory lines beginning work in December. The Führer demanded that 250 be ready for his summer 1943 offensive on the Russian Front.

Though the Panther's combat debut at Kursk in mid-1943 was a failure, with many vehicles breaking down before they got into action, once the teething problems had been ironed out it became one of the finest tanks of the war. Very fast and manoeuvrable, the Panther incorporated interleaved road wheels with torsion-bar suspension, well-sloped hull and turret, a rear engine and front drive. The long 75mm KwK42 L/70 gun was mounted in an external, curved gun mantlet with an accompanying coaxial machine gun. The turret sides and rear also featured pistol ports.

The Ausf D entered production in January 1943, with the first vehicles being allocated to units in February. In April 1943, however, deliveries stopped and all vehicles were recalled for major modifications. Then, in May, the 51st and 52nd Tank Battalions received Panthers (mostly Ausf D) and saw action at the Battle of Kursk in July 1943. The 23rd and 26th Independent Panzer Regiments received Ausf Ds, as did the élite Waffen-SS divisions.

PANZER V AUSF G

As a result of recommendations and comments from troops in the field using the Panther Ausf A and D, the Ausf G incorporated a number of design changes. Chief among them was a redesigned hull, which incorporated increased side armour on the upper-hull side and a single-piece side plate. The driver's vision port was done away with, being replaced by a rotating periscope. In addition, the driver could drive with his head out of the hatch thanks to an adjustable seat and extendible controls.

Suspension was as standard, though in September 1944 a number of vehicles were fitted with steel-rimmed "silent bloc" wheels that became standard on the Ausf F in 1945. Other modifications included armoured ammunition bins, a heater system that drew warm air from a device over the left-side engine fan, and flame-trap exhaust mufflers.

The Ausf G saw service on the Eastern Front and in the West from March 1944 to the end of the war, during which time 3126 were produced. It comprised over half the tank strength of the panzer divisions in 1945, its KwK42 L/70 gun taking a heavy toll of Soviet tanks in the fighting in East Prussia and Hungary. However, by that late stage of the war the Panthers were unable to stop the deluge of Red Army armoured units.

SPECIFICATIONS

PANZER V AUSF G

Designation:
SdKfz 171

Type:
Heavy Medium Tank

Length:
8.86m (29.06ft)

Width:
3.43m (11.25ft)

Height:
2.98m (9.77ft)

Weight:
46,327kg (101,920lb)

Crew:
Five

Main Armament:
75mm

Secondary Armament:
2 x 7.92mm

Engine:
Maybach HL230P30

Range:
200km (125 miles)

Speed:
46km/h (28.75mph)

Fording:
1.7m (5.57ft)

Trench Crossing:
1.91m (6.26ft)

Armour (hull):
80mm (3.14in)

Armour (turret):
110mm (4.33in)

PANZER 35(T)

SPECIFICATIONS

PANZER 35(T)

Designation: **Panzerkampfwagen 35(t)**	**Secondary Armament:** **2 x 7.92mm**
Type: **Light Tank**	**Engine:** **Skoda T11**
Length: **4.9m (16.07ft)**	**Range:** **190km (119 miles)**
Width: **2.1m (6.88ft)**	**Speed:** **35km/h (21.87mph)**
Height: **2.35m (7.7ft)**	**Fording:** **1m (3.25ft)**
Weight: **10,690kg (23,520lb)**	**Trench Crossing:** **1.9m (6.23ft)**
Crew: **Four**	**Armour (hull):** **25mm (.98in)**
Main Armament: **37mm**	**Armour (turret):** **25mm (.98in)**

The Panzer 35(t) was a Czech-designed tank in the 10-ton class. As well as being rugged, much thought had gone into ease of operation. Thus, a 12-speed gearbox combined with a a pneumatic-servo-mechanical steering unit to make the tank easy to drive. In addition, the suspension system, consisting of two sets of four-wheel bogie units each side, was very hard wearing.

The four-man crew sat in a single compartment, with the engine at the rear. The tank's armament, like most Czech tanks of the period, consisted of a 37mm gun (in this case the Skoda A3) plus a coaxial 7.92mm machine gun and a second machine gun in the hull front.

Approximately 160 were built for the Czech Army, having the designation LT-35. Following the annexation of Czechoslovakia by Germany, 106 of these vehicles were given to the 6th Panzer Division. During the campaign in the West in 1940, the Panzer 35(t) formed the backbone of the armoured strength of this particular unit.

Though it performed well in Poland and the West in 1939–40, the 35(t)'s shortcomings became clear in Russia. When the 6th Panzer Division fought on the Eastern Front in 1941, for example, it lost half its Panzer 35(t)s in the first six months of combat. As well as the German Army, the Panzer 35(t) was used by the armed forces of Bulgaria, Romania and Slovakia.

PANZER 38(T)

The Czech LT-38 was one of the most successful products of the pre-war Czech armaments industry. Originating as a design in 1933, it was gradually improved so that by 1938 the latest version, the TNHP, was ordered for the Czech Army. Some 150 were ordered for the Czechs, while foreign orders totalled 200.

When the Germans took over the country in March 1939, they were pleased to have the tank and continued its production as the Panzer 38(t). They were soon issued to the 7th and 8th Panzer Divisions, and by 1941 this vehicle formed nearly 25 percent of the total Wehrmacht tank strength.

The centrally placed turret, mounted on the roof of the fighting compartment, carried the Skoda 37mm A7 gun and a 7.92mm machine gun, while another machine gun was mounted in the front of the hull on the left-hand side. Rugged, reliable and easy to maintain, the Germans were happy to keep building the Panzer 38(t) until 1942, by which time a total of 1168 had been produced. By this date it was obsolete as a frontline tank, but the chassis continued to be used as a platform for self-propelled guns. Before the Germans seized Czechoslovakia, the vehicle was sold abroad or built under licence. In some countries it continued in service into the late 1940s.

SPECIFICATIONS

PANZER 38(T)

Designation: **Panzerkampfwagen 38(t)**	Secondary Armament: **2 x 7.92mm**
Type: **Light Tank**	Engine: **Praga EPA**
Length: **4.61m (15.12ft)**	Range: **250km (156 miles)**
Width: **2.13m (7ft)**	Speed: **42km/h (26.25mph)**
Height: **2.4m (7.87ft)**	Fording: **.9m (3ft)**
Weight: **9672kg (21,280lb)**	Trench Crossing: **1.87m (6.13ft)**
Crew: **Four**	Armour (hull): **25mm (.98in)**
Main Armament: **37mm**	Armour (turret): **25mm (.98in)**

PANZERJÄGER

SPECIFICATIONS

PANZERJÄGER

Designation: **Panzerjäger**	Secondary Armament: **None**
Type: **SP Antitank Gun**	Engine: **Maybach NL38TR**
Length: **4.42m (14.5ft)**	Range: **140km (87 miles)**
Width: **2.06m (6.75ft)**	Speed: **40km/h (25mph)**
Height: **2.25m (7.38ft)**	Fording: **.85m (2.78ft)**
Weight: **6516kg (14,336lb)**	Trench Crossing: **1.75m (5.74ft)**
Crew: **Three**	Armour (hull): **13mm (.51in)**
Main Armament: **47mm**	Armour (superstructure): **13mm (.51in)**

This vehicle was the first of Germany's "tank hunters", and consisted of a Czech 47mm antitank gun on a Panzer I Ausf B chassis (which by early 1940 was obsolete as a frontline tank). Some 170 tank chassis were converted by Alkett of Berlin-Spandau between March 1940 and February 1941.

The conversion was relatively simple, and involved nothing more than removing the tank turret and placing the gun and a three-sided shield in its place. The superstructure was open at the rear, and there was enough room inside for 86 rounds for the 47mm Pak(t) L43.4 gun. The latter was mounted within the shield on a pivoting mount supported by girders. The Maybach engine was driven by a gearbox that had five forward gears and one reverse.

The Panzerjäger was issued to five army antitank battalions, and it first saw action in Belgium and France in May and June 1940 during the German attack in the West. It proved adequate enough, though even at this early date it was becoming obsolete as a frontline fighting vehicle. In North Africa the vehicles saw service with the Afrika Korps in infantry antitank units, while it was also used during the initial phase of the war on the Eastern Front. It also served in Italy. In late 1943 the Panzerjäger was phased out of service.

PANZERJÄGER 38(T)

War on the Eastern Front presented many problems for the German Army, not least superior Soviet tanks, specifically the T-34. In the short term this was solved by the production of self-propelled antitank guns. The Panzerjäger 38(t) was one such vehicle.

As the Panzer 38(t) was obsolete as a battle tank and too slow for a reconnaissance vehicle, the chassis were singled out for conversion to gun carriages. An order dated 22 December 1941 called for production of 17 vehicles per month, beginning on 24 March 1942, with an increase to 30 units per month from July. A total of 344 were produced between April and October 1942, a further 19 Panzer 38(t) chassis being converted in 1943.

Armament consisted of the 76.2mm Pak 36(r) L/51.5 gun, which was the Russian FK296 gun rebuilt to fire the German Pak 40 cartridge. Large numbers of this weapon had been captured during the German invasion in June 1941.

The Panzerjäger 38(t) served mainly with antitank units on the Eastern Front, though 66 also served in North Africa with the 33rd and 39th Antitank Battalions. These vehicles arrived in-theatre between July and November 1942. Compared to later German antitank vehicles, the Panzerjäger 38(t) had a high silhouette and the crew was very exposed.

SPECIFICATIONS

PANZERJÄGER 38(T)

Designation: **Marder III**	Secondary Armament: **1 x 7.92mm**
Type: **SP Antitank Gun**	Engine: **Praga EPA**
Length: **5.85m (19.19ft)**	Range: **185km (116 miles)**
Width: **2.16m (7.08ft)**	Speed: **42km/h (26.25mph)**
Height: **2.5m (8.2ft)**	Fording: **.9m (3ft)**
Weight: **10,864kg (23,900lb)**	Trench Crossing: **1.87m (6.13ft)**
Crew: **Four**	Armour (hull): **50mm (1.96in)**
Main Armament: **76.2mm**	Armour (turret): **50mm (1.96in)**

PZKPFW M15/42

SPECIFICATIONS

PZKPFW M15/42

Designation: M15/42 738(i)	**Secondary Armament:** 1 x 8mm
Type: Medium Tank	**Engine:** 15TB V-8 petrol
Length: 5.04m (16.53ft)	**Range:** 180km (112 miles)
Width: 2.23m (7.31ft)	**Speed:** 38km/h (23.75mph)
Height: 2.39m (7.84ft)	**Fording:** 1m (3.25ft)
Weight: 14,967kg (32,928lb)	**Trench Crossing:** 2.1m (6.88ft)
Crew: Four	**Armour (hull):** 30mm (1.18in)
Main Armament: 47mm	**Armour (turret):** 49mm (1.92in)

When the Italian Army received an updated model of its medium tank, designated M15/42, the German Army reaped the rewards. The Italians quit the Axis in September 1943 (only 82 had been delivered to the Italian Army before this date), and the German Army took control of 92 of the new tanks. Overall they still had many of the faults typical of Italian armoured fighting vehicles, but they did give the Germans some sorely needed fighting vehicles in the Italian theatre.

The Panzer M15/42 featured heavier frontal armour, a petrol-powered engine (there was a severe shortage of diesel in Italy at the time), and a longer gun. The hull length was increased to accommodate the petrol engine, while the suspension bogies were moved apart to handle the extra weight. The M15/42 was distinguished from the earlier M13/40 and M14/41 models by the location of the access door on the right-hand side of the superstructure.

In German use the M15/42 was issued to three German Army panzer detachments and the 22nd SS Division *Maria Theresia* (formed from Hungarian volunteers in April 1944). Each vehicle carried 111 rounds for the tank's 47mm KwK 47/40(i) L/40 gun, and by the end of 1944 there were still 68 Italian medium tanks in German service.

PZKPFW MKII 748 (E)

German victories in the first three years of the war resulted the capture of large numbers of enemy vehicles. These were pressed into service. The problems with this was the lack of spare parts and eventual obsolescence. Due to the small numbers involved, it was not worth the setting up of spare parts manufacture, and as a result most of these vehicles were lost due to maintenance problems. French and Italian armoured vehicles could be relatively easily maintained because those countries (which Germany occupied) had large stocks of spares, but armoured vehicles captured from other adversaries presented problems.

In North Africa, the Germans captured a large number of British armoured vehicles. They were used by the Afrika Korps until they were lost. One such vehicle was the Matilda, which in German use was designated Infanterie Panzerkampfwagen Mk II 748(e). Ironically the Germans only lost their Matildas through lack of maintenance, as no British tank then in North Africa was capable of knocking it out. In Europe, a number of captured Matildas were stripped of their turrets and converted to self-propelled guns by mounting the 50mm KwK L/42 gun. These vehicles had been captured by the Germans in 1940. However, they were only used by garrison forces stationed near the stockpiled dumps.

SPECIFICATIONS

PZKPFW MKII 748 (E)

Designation:
PzKpfw Mk II 748 (E)

Type:
Infantry Tank

Length:
5.63m (18.5ft)

Width:
2.59m (8.5ft)

Height:
2.44m (8ft)

Weight:
26,981kg (59,360lb)

Crew:
Four

Main Armament:
2pdr

Secondary Armament:
1 x 7.92mm

Engine:
Leyland diesel 190hp

Range:
257km (160 miles)

Speed:
24km/h (15mph)

Fording:
.9m (3ft)

Trench Crossing:
2.13m (7ft)

Armour (hull):
20mm (.78in)

Armour (turret):
78mm (3in)

COMET

In 1943, work began on developing a successor to the Cromwell and Challenger tanks, under the General Staff specification A34. The design was based on technology used in the Cromwell, and it was intended that the new vehicle would be armed with the Vickers 75mm gun. However, for reasons of communality the 17-pounder model was chosen, being modified by Vickers. The weapon was designated as the "Gun, QF, Tank 77mm". The title "77mm" was adopted to avoid confusion with other 3in guns which were entering British and US service.

Production of the Comet began in the autumn of 1944, and by January 1945 143 vehicles had been built. Comprising an all-welded hull and a turret which was part cast and part rolled plate, it was mechanically identical to the Cromwell. Though slower than the latter, its main gun was more powerful then the Cromwell's, especially when firing the new armoured-piercing, discarding sabot round, which had a muzzle velocity of 1097m/sec (3600ft/sec).

The Comet saw action in Germany in March–May 1945, right at the end of the war in Europe, and was judged a great success, being more reliable than either the Challenger or Cromwell. The Comet remained in British Army service until the mid-1960s.

SPECIFICATIONS

COMET

Designation:
Cruiser Tank Comet

Type:
Heavy Cruiser Tank

Length:
7.65m (25.1ft)

Width:
3.04m (10ft)

Height:
2.66m (8.75ft)

Weight:
33,090kg (72,800lb)

Crew:
Five

Main Armament:
77mm

Secondary Armament:
2 x 7.92mm

Engine:
Meteor 600hp

Range:
250km (156.25 miles)

Speed:
18km/h (29mph)

Fording:
1.12m (4ft)

Trench Crossing:
2.28m (7.5ft)

Armour (hull):
25mm (.98in)

Armour (turret):
101mm (3.97in)

CROMWELL

SPECIFICATIONS

CROMWELL

Designation:
Cruiser Tank Mk VIII

Type:
Cruiser Tank

Length:
6.33m (20.8ft)

Width:
3.04m (10ft)

Height:
2.5 m (8.2ft)

Weight:
28,509kg (67,720lb)

Crew:
Five

Main Armament:
75mm

Secondary Armament:
1 x 7.92mm

Engine:
Meteor 600hp

Range:
278km (173 miles)

Speed:
64km/h (40mph)

Fording:
1.21m (4ft)

Trench Crossing:
2.28m (7.5ft)

Armour (hull):
8mm (.31in)

Armour (turret):
76mm (2.99in)

British cruiser tanks were designed to be relatively fast and lightly armoured to assume the cavalry role on the battlefield: to exploit gaps punched in enemy defences by the heavier infantry tanks, and then penetrate far behind enemy lines in the way horsed cavalry did in earlier periods.

There were a number of cruiser tanks manufactured by the British. Two versions of the Cruiser Tank Mk VIII developed were the A27L (Centaur) and the A27M Cromwell. Designed by the Birmingham Railway Carriage and Wagon Company, the Cromwell was powered by the new Rolls-Royce Meteor engine (hence the "M" in the designation).

The design of the tank is interesting. It had first been drawn up in 1940, and as a result of experience in the North African war some outmoded construction practices and design features were included. These included a slab-sided hull and turret in preference to sloped armour, a bolted and riveted design rather than welded, and a shoulder-controlled main gun/coaxial armament rather than a mechanical geared system. The shoulder-controlled system had been introduced in the 1930s as a means of firing relatively accurately on the move (with slow tanks it was adequate enough, but it was woefully deficient when tank speeds increased).

CROMWELL MK VI

By the time of the invasion of France in June 1944, the Cromwell was the most important British tank in service. Fast and well armed, it was still under-armed when compared to the fearsome German Panthers and Tigers it came into contact with in Normandy. Nevertheless, it was reliable and by equipping their armoured reconnaissance units with Cromwells the British in effect added an extra medium tank battalion to their armoured divisions.

Fast the Cromwell may have been, but when it came to tank-versus-tank action it suffered alarmingly. An example was Operation Goodwood, launched in Normandy on 18 July 1944, during which an estimated 1350 British tanks came to blows with 400 German armoured vehicles (most of which were in hull-down positions). It has been described as a "tactical holocaust", and indeed losses were fearful. German tanks, firing from good positions at optimum ranges, destroyed 300 British tanks in 72 hours.

The Cromwell had been produced in large numbers, with manufacture beginning in 1943. The above illustration shows the Cromwell VI close-support version armed with a 95mm howitzer. And, despite its overall shortcomings, the Cromwell VI and VIII remained in service with British Army regiments until the 1950s.

SPECIFICATIONS

CROMWELL MK VI

Designation: **Cruiser Tank Mk VI**	Secondary Armament: **1 x 7.92mm**
Type: **Cruiser Tank**	Engine: **Meteor 600hp**
Length: **6.33m (20.8ft)**	Range: **250km (156.25 miles)**
Width: **3.04m (10ft)**	Speed: **64km/h (40mph)**
Height: **2.5 m (8.2ft)**	Fording: **1.21m (4ft)**
Weight: **28,509kg (67,720lb)**	Trench Crossing: **2.28m (7.5ft)**
Crew: **Five**	Armour (hull): **8mm (.31in)**
Main Armament: **95mm**	Armour (turret): **76mm (2.99in)**

CHALLENGER

SPECIFICATIONS

CHALLENGER

Designation: **Cruiser Tank Challenger**	Secondary Armament: **1 x 7.92mm**
Type: **Cruiser Tank**	Engine: **Meteor 600hp**
Length: **8m (26.3ft)**	Range: **260km (162.5 miles)**
Width: **2.89m (9.5ft)**	Speed: **51km/h (32mph)**
Height: **2.66m (8.75ft)**	Fording: **1.21m (4ft)**
Weight: **32,581kg (71,680lb)**	Trench Crossing: **2.28m (7.5ft)**
Crew: **Five**	Armour (hull): **20mm (.78in)**
Main Armament: **17pdr**	Armour (turret): **102mm (4in)**

The Challenger was the result of a further development of the Cromwell tank under the General Staff Specification A30. It was designed to mount the new 17-pounder high-velocity antitank gun, and it came into service in 1944.

It had been originally thought that the Centaur/Comet chassis could used for the Challenger, but weight and size of the gun and turret meant a redesigned chassis. The result was a longer, wider vehicle with a high turret, very long gun, widened centre hull and Christie suspension. Some 200 were built in total, 12 being allocated to each armoured regiment, and they saw limited service in Europe in 1944–45.

Great things were expected of the Challenger, but in service it proved something of a disappointment. It was under-armoured and difficult to steer due to its increased length (there was no corresponding increase in width between track centres, thus the ratio of length to width was increased to unacceptable levels). In addition, the Challenger was unable to engage the Panther and Tiger on equal terms. A parallel development – the mounting of the 17-pounder in the Sherman – proved more of a success, and the resultant vehicle, the Sherman Firefly, ultimately took over the role envisaged for the Challenger.

CRUISER TANK MK I

The early British tanks in the cruiser category did not have names, but were merely known by their General Staff designation ("A") numbers. The A9, together with the A10 and A13, was one of first to reach the army in 1938.

The main armament of the A9 was the two-pounder gun, which was the standard armament of all British cruiser and infantry tanks up to 1942. In 1930 the two-pounder was reckoned to be one of the best tank guns in the world, though it was rapidly outclassed as the war progressed. To increase its armour penetration, it was fitted with a Littlejohn squeeze muzzle attachment for firing armour-piercing, composite non-rigid rounds. However, this provided only a temporary respite.

The design of the A9 was unusual, and incorporated three-wheel bogies, power traverse for the turret, and two auxiliary machine-gun turrets. Machine guns initially consisted of .303in Vickers water-cooled guns coaxially with the main gun, with two other .303in Vickers in the turrets. It shared the same Carden-designed running gear, engine, transmission and main armament found in the A10 and A13. The hull was essentially an oblong box carried between the tracks. The A9 was in service 1938–41. Despite its innovative design, it was too lightly armed to take on comparable German tanks.

SPECIFICATIONS

CRUISER TANK MK I

Designation:
Cruiser Tank Mk I (A9)

Type:
Cruiser Tank

Length:
5.86m (19.25ft)

Width:
2.53m (8.33ft)

Height:
2.52m (8.3ft)

Weight:
12,218kg (26,880lb)

Crew:
Six

Main Armament:
2pdr

Secondary Armament:
3 x .330in

Engine:
AEG 150hp

Range:
210km (131.25 miles)

Speed:
40km/h (25mph)

Fording:
.9m (3ft)

Trench Crossing:
2.26m (7.41ft)

Armour (hull):
6mm (.23in)

Armour (turret):
14mm (.55in)

CRUISER TANK MK IV

SPECIFICATIONS

CRUISER TANK MK IV

Designation: **Cruiser Tank Mk IV**	Secondary Armament: **1 x .303in**
Type: **Cruiser Tank**	Engine: **Liberty 340hp**
Length: **6m (19.75ft)**	Range: **232km (144 miles)**
Width: **2.53m (8.33ft)**	Speed: **48km/h (30mph)**
Height: **2.59m (8.5ft)**	Fording: **.9m (3ft)**
Weight: **14,254kg (31,360lb)**	Trench Crossing: **2.26m (7.41ft)**
Crew: **Four**	Armour (hull): **6mm (.23in)**
Main Armament: **2pdr**	Armour (turret): **30mm (1.18in)**

The Cruiser Tank Mk IV (A13) originated in 1936 following British War Office observers witnessing the high speed of the Christie-type BT tanks in Soviet service. The Nuffield company was therefore asked to design a tank based on the Christie design to replace the A9 and A10.

The resulting Cruiser Tank Mk III had high speed, Christie suspension and a high power-to-weight ratio. The Mk IV was an up-armoured version of the Mk III, with the addition of extra armoured plates and an armour thickness of 20-30mm (.78-1.18in). The Mk IV was in production by 1938, and was used by the British Expeditionary Force (BEF) in France in 1940.

The distinctive design feature of the A13 tanks was their flat-sided turrets. Another design feature was different-shaped mantlets. The Cruiser Tank Mk IVA had an axle-shaped mantlet, while other Mk IVs had rectangular-shaped mantlets. All the Cruiser Tanks went to France with the BEF with high hopes. However, once they got there their performance left a lot to be desired. They were found to be unreliable, underpowered, under-armoured and had tracks that were too narrow and came off too easily. That said, in North Africa in 1941 their performance improved (no doubt a dryer climate and regular maintenance were the reasons).

CRUISER TANK MK V

The Mk V Covenanter was designed to use as many parts of the A13 as possible. The new vehicle was designated the A13 Mk III, Cruiser Tank Mk V, and immediately it had a host of problems. They were mainly to do with the engine, which was the only untried feature. The cooling system was particularly irksome, and required army workshops modifying the engine air intake louvres, which were located at the front left-hand side, next to the driver. The tanks thus modified were known as Covenanter Mk IIs.

The Covenanter was in service by 1940, and in 1941 two further models appeared – the Mk III and IV – but the cooling system problem was never properly resolved and so the Covenanter was finally declared unfit for overseas service.

Despite its shortcomings, the Covenanter played an important part in the defence of Great Britain, first helping to re-equip those units that had lost their tanks in the defeat in France in 1940 (the British Army had left nearly all of its heavy equipment behind during the evacuation from Dunkirk), and then contributing to the new armoured divisions being raised. The 9th Armoured Division, for example, was almost exclusively equipped with Covenanters. Despite its problems, 1771 vehicles were built and they saw home service up to 1943.

SPECIFICATIONS

CRUISER TANK MK V

Designation: **Cruiser Tank Mk V**	Secondary Armament: **1 x 7.92mm**
Type: **Cruiser Tank**	Engine: **Meadows Flat-12 300hp**
Length: **5.79m (19ft)**	Range: **200km (125 miles)**
Width: **2.62m (8.6ft)**	Speed: **50km/h (31mph)**
Height: **2.22m (7.3ft)**	Fording: **1m (3.25ft)**
Weight: **18,327kg (40,320lb)**	Trench Crossing: **1.52m (4.98ft)**
Crew: **Four**	Armour (hull): **7mm (.27in)**
Main Armament: **2pdr**	Armour (turret): **40mm (1.57in)**

CRUISER TANK MK VII

SPECIFICATIONS

CRUISER TANK MK VII

Designation:
Cruiser Tank Mk VII

Secondary Armament:
2 x 7.92mm

Type:
Cruiser Tank

Engine:
Liberty 410hp

Length:
6.33m (19.8ft)

Range:
200km (125 miles)

Width:
2.89m (9.5ft)

Speed:
38.4km/h (24mph)

Height:
2.4m (8ft)

Fording:
1m (3.25ft)

Weight:
26,981kg (59,360lb)

Trench Crossing:
2.59m (8.49ft)

Crew:
Five

Armour (hull):
20mm (.78in)

Main Armament:
6pdr

Armour (turret):
76mm (3in)

An enlarged version of the Covenanter was the A13 Mk III, which was called the Crusader. By late 1942 this tank was obsolete, and so was temporarily succeeded by the Cruiser Tank Mk VII (A24). This vehicle was originally named the Cromwell I, but was later renamed the Cavalier.

The tank had the six-pounder as its main armament, which was an effective antitank weapon when it entered service (though it lacked a high-explosive round throughout most of its service life), with a coaxial BESA machine gun plus another BESA in the hull. The 7.92mm BESA was built under licence by the company BSA. It was developed from the Czech ZB37, and was an accurate and reliable weapon, though rather bulky for a tank and requiring a large opening in the tank's armour. Nevertheless, it was the standard British armoured fighting vehicle armament in World War II.

The Cavalier was an interim until the Cromwell was developed, and because of this only 50 were built. These were used for training purposes only. Externally the Cavalier was almost identical to the Centaur and Cavalier, with Christie suspension and rectangular hull and turret. The Cavalier entered service in 1942 and continued in its training role until the end of the war, providing a valuable role of familiarization.

CRUSADER III

Designed and manufactured by Nuffield Mechanisation & Aero, the Cruiser Tank Mk VI (A15) Crusader was, like the Covenanter, armed with the two-pounder main gun. Auxiliary weapons consisted of two 7.92mm BESA machine guns, one mounted coaxially with the main gun and the other in a small turret on the forward hull roof, next to the driver.

The Crusader design shared many common components with the Covenanter. It was ordered in July 1939, and became one of the main British tanks until production ceased in 1943. By that time numbers built totalled 5300.

The Crusader was used extensively in the North African war, where it suffered from a number of mechanical problems. In addition, the Crusader's light armour was also a major disadvantage when it came up against German panzers. The Crusader was produced in a number of variants. The Crusader I CS was a close-support model armed with a 3in howitzer in place of the two-pounder gun. The Crusader II had additional armour, while the Crusader II CS was again a close-support vehicle armed with the 3in howitzer. The Crusader III, illustrated above, was the final production model and was armed with the six-pounder main gun in place of the two-pounder.

SPECIFICATIONS

CRUSADER III

Designation: **Cruiser Tank Mk VI**	*Secondary Armament:* **2 x 7.92mm**
Type: **Cruiser Tank**	*Engine:* **Nuffield Liberty 340hp**
Length: **6m (19.68ft)**	*Range:* **204km (127 miles)**
Width: **2.64m (8.66ft)**	*Speed:* **50km/h (31mph)**
Height: **2.23m (7.31ft)**	*Fording:* **.9m (3.25ft)**
Weight: **20,067kg (44,147lb)**	*Trench Crossing:* **2.59m (8.49ft)**
Crew: **Three**	*Armour (hull):* **7mm (.27in)**
Main Armament: **6pdr**	*Armour (turret):* **40mm (1.57in)**

GRANT MEDIUM TANK

SPECIFICATIONS

GRANT MEDIUM TANK

Designation:
Grant Medium Tank

Secondary Armament:
1 x 37mm

Type:
Medium Tank

Engine:
Wright Continental R-975

Length:
5.63m (18.5ft)

Range:
257km (160 miles)

Width:
2.51m (8.5ft)

Speed:
41.6km/h (26mph)

Height:
2.81m (9.25ft)

Fording:
1.02m (3.34ft)

Weight:
27,272kg (60,000lb)

Trench Crossing:
1.91m (6.26ft)

Crew:
Six

Armour (hull):
38.1mm (1.5in)

Main Armament:
75mm

Armour (turret):
12.7mm (.5in)

Under the terms of the Lend-Lease scheme, the British purchased a number of Medium Tank M3s from the US government. The vehicle was slightly modified, as the British Tank Commission requested a modification to suit British requirements. This entailed changes to the turret, which was longer than the M3 version, with a prominent rear overhang to allow for the installation of wireless equipment in the turret rear.

The vehicle's silhouette, somewhat high, was reduced by doing away with the cupola, and the turret itself was reduced by at least 305mm (12in) – although the end result was still an excellent target for antitank gunners. The M3 was a vehicle of necessity, as the Americans produced it believing that future tanks would require a main gun of not less than 75mm calibre, but at the time – 1941 – they were unable to produce a fully rotating turret to house such a weapon. Thus the 75mm gun was housed in a hull sponson, while the rotating turret housed a 37mm gun.

The M3 in British service was known as the Grant after the American Civil War general U.S. Grant. The Grant Canal Defence Light version was not a tank but an armoured housing with a powerful searchlight in the place of the original tank turret to light up the battlefield during night actions.

INFANTRY TANK MK II

The Infantry Tank Mk II Matilda was designed as an immediate replacement for the Infantry Tank Mk I, Matilda I, as the latter was totally inadequate for its intended role. The prototype was first tested in April 1938, and it proved to be one of the best tanks at this time. However, it was a complicated tank and not really suited to mass production. The fact that only two were in service when war broke out in September 1939 is testament to its production problems.

The tank's main armament was the two-pounder gun, with a coaxial BESA machine gun and two single-shot smoke bomb throwers mounted externally on the turret side and operated by cable from within the turret. The Matilda was relatively small, but because of its heavy cast hull and side skirts it appeared massive. Some 2987 were produced between 1940 and 1943, some being sent as aid to the Soviet Union.

In service the Matilda proved useful. In France, in 1940, German 37mm antitank rounds bounced off its hull, and in North Africa in 1940 it helped to smash Italian artillery and armour. There were also a number of special purpose derivatives built, such as the Matilda Scorpion, a tank flail device designed to clear a path through enemy minefields by beating on the ground as the vehicle advanced.

SPECIFICATIONS

INFANTRY TANK MK II

Designation: **Infantry Tank Mk II**	Secondary Armament: **1 x 7.92mm**
Type: **Infantry Tank**	Engine: **Leyland Diesel 190hp**
Length: **5.63m (18.5ft)**	Range: **257km (160 miles)**
Width: **2.59m (8.5ft)**	Speed: **24km/h (15mph)**
Height: **2.44m (8ft)**	Fording: **.9m (3ft)**
Weight: **26,981kg (59,360lb)**	Trench Crossing: **2.13m (7ft)**
Crew: **Four**	Armour (hull): **20mm (.78in)**
Main Armament: **2pdr**	Armour (turret): **78mm (3in)**

LIGHT TANK MK VI

SPECIFICATIONS

LIGHT TANK MK VI

Designation:
Light Tank Mk VI

Type:
Light Tank

Length:
4.02m (13.2ft)

Width:
2.08m (6.83ft)

Height:
2.28m (7.5ft)

Weight:
5294kg (11,648lb)

Crew:
Three

Main Armament:
1 x .303in, 1 x .5in

Secondary Armament:
None

Engine:
Meadows ESTB/A 88hp

Range:
200km (125 miles)

Speed:
56km/h (35mph)

Fording:
.9m (3ft)

Trench Crossing:
1.52m (4.98ft)

Armour (hull):
4mm (.15in)

Armour (turret):
14mm (.59in)

Designed by Vickers Armstrong Ltd, the Light Tank Mk VI was the culmination of a long series of Light Tanks stemming from the Carden-Loyd Mk VIII. It followed the pattern of its predecessors and had its engine in the right-hand side of the hull, with the transmission led forward to drive the front sprockets. The driver sat in the left-hand side, while the turret, containing the commander and gunner, was also off-set to the left.

The suspension consisted of two-wheeled bogie units each side, sprung on twin coil springs, the rear wheel acting also as a trailing idler. This arrangement was simple and dependable, though the tracks had a nasty tendency to shed themselves at speed.

Armament consisted of two machine guns – a Vickers .5in and a water-cooled .303in Vickers – and armour thickness was poor. The Mk VI was actually no more than a reconnaissance vehicle, though the British Army used it as a battle tank in 1940 because of the delay in the delivery of Cruiser tanks. Needless to say, they were no match for the German tanks they came up against in France, and suffered accordingly. Mk VIBs and earlier light tanks were also used in the early campaigns in North Africa, where they fared better against equally poor Italian tanks.

MEDIUM TANK MK II

The Medium Tank Mk II first appeared in 1925, being more heavily armoured than the Mk I and its suspension being protected by armoured side skirts. When it first appeared it was a formidable armoured fighting vehicle, and was actually a world leader in tank design. The Mk II was in service until 1939 and was thereafter used for training purposes.

The Mk II* had a coaxial Vickers machine gun in the turret but no Hotchkiss machine guns, though a commander's cupola was added. The Mk II** was a Mk II conversion, having twin mountings for the three-pounder gun and a Vickers .303in machine gun. Some 44 vehicles were thus converted. The Medium Tank Mk IIA was produced in 1930 by Vickers Armstrong Ltd, but only 20 were built. The bevel was removed from the rear of the turret and a command cupola was fitted. Other modifications included better suspension units with rearranged track-return rollers.

A close-support version was the Medium Tank Mk IIA CS, which was armed with a 3.7in howitzer. Five tanks were converted for service in tropical conditions, having sun screens consisting of woven asbestos. They were fitted outside the upper surfaces and sides of the tank. The bridge-laying version of the tank was fitted with side brackets to carry bridge girders.

SPECIFICATIONS

MEDIUM TANK MK II

Designation:
Medium Tank Mk II

Type:
Medium Tank

Length:
5.33m (17.5ft)

Width:
2.77m (9.1ft)

Height:
2.68m (8.8ft)

Weight:
13,440kg (29,568lb)

Crew:
Five

Main Armament:
3pdr

Secondary Armament:
6 x .303in

Engine:
Armstrong-Siddeley 90hp

Range:
257km (160 miles)

Speed:
24km/h (15mph)

Fording:
.85m (2.9ft)

Trench Crossing:
1.75m (5.75ft)

Armour (hull):
8.25mm (.32in)

Armour (turret):
8.25mm (.32in)

SHERMAN FIREFLY

SPECIFICATIONS

SHERMAN FIREFLY

Designation:
Sherman Firefly

Secondary Armament:
1 x .3in, 1 x .5in

Type:
Medium Tank

Engine:
Ford V-8 500hp

Length:
6.27m (20.57ft)

Range:
160km (100 miles)

Width:
2.68m (8.79ft)

Speed:
47km/h (29mph)

Height:
3.43m (11.25ft)

Fording:
.9m (3ft)

Weight:
32,284kg (71,024lb)

Trench Crossing:
2.26m (7.41ft)

Crew:
Five

Armour (hull):
15mm (.59in)

Main Armament:
17pdr

Armour (turret):
100mm (3.93in)

In 1943 it was decided to mount the British high-velocity 17-pounder gun in the Sherman medium tank to give the vehicle some "punch" against German Tigers and Panthers. This required the turret being modified and the gun being mounted on its side and adapted for left-hand loading.

The gun filled most of the turret, so an aperture had to be cut in the rear of the turret and an armoured box was added. This acted as a counterweight and contained the tank's radio sets. An additional hatch for the loader was cut in the turret roof, as the gun breech obstructed his exit through the commander's rotating roof hatch. To make room inside the hull, the hull gunner's position was done away with, the bow machine gun was removed, the aperture plated over and an ammunition bin replaced the seat. Each vehicle could thus carry 78 rounds for the main gun.

Most Fireflies were converted from Sherman Vs. The Ordnance, QF, 17-pounder was originally developed as a towed antitank gun. It was too heavy for manhandling in the field, and was too large for mounting in British tanks when it entered service in 1942. It was mounted on the Cruiser, though with some difficulty, but was more easily adapted for the Sherman, and some 600 of the latter vehicles were so modified.

VALENTINE II

Because the proposal for this infantry tank was sent to the War Office just before St. Valentine's Day 1938, it was named after the saint's day thereafter. The Valentine was in fact one of the most reliable of British tanks, being based on the A9 and A10 tanks. Both hull and turret were more compact, but this limited the vehicle to a three-man crew.

The first contract, for 275 tanks, was placed with Vickers Armstrong, with a further 125 being ordered from the Metropolitan-Cammell Carriage & Wagon Company Ltd and 200 more from the Birmingham Railway Carriage & Wagon Company Ltd. When war broke out Valentine production rose steadily, and by mid-1941 they were being delivered at a rate of 45 per month. They were issued in lieu of Cruiser tanks to equip some of the new armoured divisions that were formed after the Dunkirk evacuation.

The Valentine was developed through several models. The Mk I was the original vehicle; the Mk II had an AEC six-cylinder engine instead of the petrol one. Armament for the early Valentines consisted of a two-pounder gun. Though home defence was the primary role of the tank in 1940–41, some were sent to North Africa at the end of 1941. A total of 8275 had been built by the time production ceased in 1944.

SPECIFICATIONS

VALENTINE II

Designation:
Infantry Tank Mk III

Type:
Infantry Tank

Length:
5.41m (17.75ft)

Width:
2.62m (8.59ft)

Height:
2.28m (7.5ft)

Weight:
17,309kg (38,080lb)

Crew:
Three

Main Armament:
2pdr

Secondary Armament:
1 x 7.92mm

Engine:
GM diesel 138hp

Range:
145km (90 miles)

Speed:
24km/h (15mph)

Fording:
.9m (3ft)

Trench Crossing:
2.28m (7.48ft)

Armour (hull):
8mm (.31in)

Armour (turret):
65mm (2.55in)

CARRO ARMATO M11/39

SPECIFICATIONS

CARRO ARMATO M11/39

Designation:
Carro Armato M11/39

Type:
Medium Tank

Length:
4.72m (15.5ft)

Width:
2.15m (7.08ft)

Height:
2.23m (7.33ft)

Weight:
11,200 kg (24,640lb)

Crew:
Three

Main Armament:
37mm

Secondary Armament:
2 x 8mm

Engine:
Spa 8T 105hp

Range:
200km (125 miles)

Speed:
32km/h (20mph)

Fording:
1m (3.25ft)

Trench Crossing:
2.1m (6.88ft)

Armour (hull):
6mm (.23in)

Armour (turret):
30mm (1.18in)

The first prototype of the M11/39 was built in 1937. It had a suspension system scaled up from that of the L3/35, a rear engine with drive sprockets at the front, a 37mm gun in the front right-hand side of the hull, a driver's compartment on the left, and a machine-gun turret on the hull roof.

Suspension for the tank consisted of two four-wheel bogie units each side. Each group of four wheels was in two pairs, controlled by a single semi-elliptic leaf spring. The powerplant was an excellent V-form eight-cylinder diesel engine, which produced a top speed of 32km/h (20mph). The hull gun was a semi-automatic weapon based on an old Vickers design, though it had only a limited traverse. Turret armament consisted of twin 8mm Breda machine guns in a two mounting.

Despite its mechanical reliability, the M11/39 was a poor fighting machine due to its ineffectual armament. This did not matter when the Italians were fighting poorly armed African troops, but against more modern armies it suffered badly.

It was used in Libya in 1940, though by this time it was obsolete. Many tanks were easily knocked out by British guns and the tank was swiftly withdrawn from service. A few captured vehicles were used by the Australians in North Africa in early 1941.

CARRO ARMATO M13/40

The M13/40 was a great improvement on the M11/39 due to its more powerful main gun and fully rotating turret. The prototype appeared in early 1940, and production was speeded up as Italy was about to enter the war. The first production vehicles rolled off the assembly line in July.

The lower hull was almost identical to that of the M11/39, although the engine was improved to give 125hp. The steering and final drive systems were also improved to give a more compact and efficient layout. The suspension system was strengthened to carry the greater weight of the vehicle by adding an extra leaf to the semi-elliptic springs.

The main armament consisted of the Ansaldo-built 47mm gun with a coaxial Breda 8mm machine gun in a hydraulically traversed turret. In addition, two Breda 38 machine guns were set in a twin mounting in the front right-hand side of the hull. Some models were further modified to take an up-rated Spa 15T engine which gave a higher speed.

The M13/40 was first used in action in North Africa in December 1940. Although inferior to comparable German tanks, it was at least equal to British cruiser tanks of the period and put up a very credible performance. A total of 1960 were built.

SPECIFICATIONS

CARRO ARMATO M13/40

Designation: **Carro Armato M13/40**	Secondary Armament: **2 x 8mm**
Type: **Medium Tank**	Engine: **Spa 15T 145hp**
Length: **4.93m (16.18ft)**	Range: **200km (125 miles)**
Width: **2.15m (7.08ft)**	Speed: **35.2km/h (22mph)**
Height: **2.37m (7.8ft)**	Fording: **1m (3.25ft)**
Weight: **14,254kg (31,360lb)**	Trench Crossing: **2.1m (6.88ft)**
Crew: **Three**	Armour (hull): **30mm (1.18in)**
Main Armament: **47mm**	Armour (turret): **40mm (1.57in)**

CARRO VELOCE 33

SPECIFICATIONS

CARRO VELOCE 33

Designation:
Carro Veloce 33

Type:
Tankette

Length:
3.16m (10.4ft)

Width:
1.7m (5.6ft)

Height:
1.29m (4.25ft)

Weight:
3207kg (7056lb)

Crew:
Two

Main Armament:
2 x 8mm

Secondary Armament:
None

Engine:
20hp

Range:
185km (115 miles)

Speed:
41.6km/h (26mph)

Fording:
.5m (1.64ft)

Trench Crossing:
1.4m (4.59ft)

Armour (hull):
15mm (.59in)

Armour (superstructure):
5mm (.19in)

Designed by Ansaldo, this vehicle closely resembled the Carro Veloce 29 tankette. The latter had been designed to accompany infantry and for general reconnaissance duties, and was in reality nothing more than a machine-gun carrier. The design of the 33 was finalised in 1933, and the Italian government, pleased with the design, placed an initial order for 1300 vehicles, which was later increased.

There were numerous variants and improved models, and it was widely used by the Italians and exported to a number of countries. Because of its light weight it could be carried by an aircraft, and on the ground could tow a tracked ammunition trailer. Its design was distinguished by being very low and small, and its lack of a turret meant the guns had to be set in the superstructure. The hull was of a rivetted and bolted construction, with the engine placed in the rear.

Other users of this vehicle included Afghanistan, Albania, Austria (illustrated above), Bolivia, Brazil, Bulgaria, China, Greece, Hungary, Iraq and Spain.

Variants included the 33/II, which had twin 8mm machine guns and improved vision ports, a version with a water-cooled machine gun. The L38 had stronger suspension, new tracks and some were fitted with a 20mm antitank gun.

L 35/LF

The basis of the L3/35 tankette was a Carden-Loyd Mk VI vehicle, 25 of which were purchased by the Italian Army in 1929. Based on these, a model known as the Carro Veloce ("fast tank") CV 28 was built by the Fiat motor works in conjunction with the Ansaldo armaments concern. This was followed by further models: CV 29 and CV L3/33. The Carro L3/35 was the final model.

The transmission was led forward to the clutch and gearbox, which had four forward speeds, in front of the driver, with final drive to front track sprockets. The fighting compartment was in the centre, with two crew members – driver on the right and gunner on the left – sitting side by side.

The L35/Lf was a flamethrower conversion of any of the three production types. Each vehicle towed a 500kg (1100lb) armoured fuel trailer, while the flame gun was mounted in the hull, replacing the machine guns. On some later vehicles the fuel tank was mounted on the rear superstructure. The range of the flame gun was approximately 100m (328ft). Though this vehicle was obsolete by 1929, it fought in North Africa in 1940–41 and some even saw service on the Eastern Front. Needless to say, for a vehicle that could be knocked out by the smallest antitank gun, they were easy prey for Red Army antitank gunners.

SPECIFICATIONS

L 35/LF

Designation: **Carro Armato L35/Lf**	Secondary Armament: **None**
Type: **Flamethrower**	Engine: **20hp**
Length: **3.16m (10.4ft)**	Range: **150km (93.75 miles)**
Width: **1.7m (5.6ft)**	Speed: **41.6km/h (26mph)**
Height: **1.29m (4.25ft)**	Fording: **.5m (1.64ft)**
Weight: **3207kg (7056lb)**	Trench Crossing: **1.4m (4.59ft)**
Crew: **Two**	Armour (hull): **15mm (.59in)**
Main Armament: **Flame Gun**	Armour (turret): **5mm (.19in)**

SEMOVENTE M40

SPECIFICATIONS

SEMOVENTE M40/41

Designation:
Semovente M40/41

Type:
Self-propelled Gun

Length:
4.91m (16.1ft)

Width:
2.28m (7.48ft)

Height:
1.85m (6.06ft)

Weight:
13,643kg (30,016lb)

Crew:
Three

Main Armament:
75mm

Secondary Armament:
None

Engine:
140km (87.5 miles)

Range:
150km (93.75 miles)

Speed:
34km/h (21.25mph)

Fording:
1m (3.25ft)

Trench Crossing:
2.1m (6.88ft)

Armour (hull):
14mm (.55in)

Armour (turret):
30mm (1.18in)

This self-propelled gun mounted the 75mm cannon, and as such it was a useful vehicle in tank-versus-tank actions. However, it proved woefully inadequate against T-34s and KV-1s on the Eastern Front.

The Italian presence on the Russian frontline was large in terms of men, but totally marginal in terms of armoured resources. The CSIR (Corpo di Spedizione Italiano in Russia), a 60,000-strong corps, and later the ARMIR (Armata Italiana in Russia), a 200,000-strong army, between them, and during the whole of their time in Russia, could muster only 55 L33/35 light tanks of the Gruppo Squadroni Carri Veloci "S.Giorgio" (a cavalry unit of the 3 Divisione Celere), 60 L6/40 light tanks of the 67th Battaglione Bersaglieri, and some 15 Semovente self-propelled guns.

The light tanks, being absolutely useless when it came to combat with other tanks, were used as support to infantry and mountain infantry units. All the tanks and the SP guns disappeared during the disastrous retreat in the southern sector of the Eastern Front in late 1942 and early 1943 following (more than 100,000 Italian soldiers died or were reported as missing in action) the fall of Stalingrad. The M40 did prove useful in North Africa against light British tanks, though, and was still being used in that theatre in early 1943.

SHI-KI

A variant of the Type 97 tank, the SHI-KI version served as a command vehicle for Japanese armoured regiments. It had the 37mm gun situated in the hull front in place of the machine gun. Another version mounted a 57mm gun duplicated in the hull front. The chief features of the tank were improvements in vision, communications and the incorporation of a directing device. The distinctive physical feature was the frame-type radio aerial around the turret.

Another variant of the Type 97 was a recovery vehicle. It was designed and equipped for rapid recovery of disabled vehicles and was built by Mitsubishi. The recovery equipment itself was simple: a rear light jib for lifting and steel ropes for towing. The tank's turret was conical-shaped. The mine-clearing version consisted of two revolving drums carrying rows of chains which exploded mines on contact. The main gun was retained in the turret.

The Type 97 had a bell-crank suspension with helical springs but no shock absorbers. The four centre wheels were mounted in pairs and operated against horizontally mounted compression springs, while the front and rear wheels acted on slopingly mounted compression springs. Drive was carried through a four-speed sliding gearbox combined with a high-and-low transfer case.

SPECIFICATIONS

COMMAND TANK SHI-KI

Designation: **Command Tank**	Secondary Armament: **None**
Type: **Medium Tank**	Engine: **Diesel V-12 170hp**
Length: **5.48m (18ft)**	Range: **230km (143.75 miles)**
Width: **5.48m (18ft)**	Speed: **37.6km/h (23.5mph)**
Height: **2.23m (7.33ft)**	Fording: **.8m (2.62ft)**
Weight: **15,272kg (33,600lb)**	Trench Crossing: **2.6m (8.53ft)**
Crew: **Four**	Armour (hull): **8mm (.31in)**
Main Armament: **37mm**	Armour (turret): **25mm (.98in)**

TYPE 94

SPECIFICATIONS

TYPE 94

Designation:
Tankette Type 94 TK

Type:
Tankette

Length:
3m (10ft)

Width:
1.62m (5.33ft)

Height:
1.62m (5.33ft)

Weight:
3563kg (7840lb)

Crew:
Two

Main Armament:
7.7mm

Secondary Armament:
None

Engine:
Four-cylinder petrol 32hp

Range:
160km (100 miles)

Speed:
40km/h (25mph)

Fording:
Unknown

Trench Crossing:
Unknown

Armour (hull):
4mm (.15in)

Armour (turret):
12mm (.47in)

The Type 94 was the result of a request from the Japanese Army in the early 1930s for an armoured tractor able to pull a tracked trailer for supplying ammunition to troops in the forward battle area. Its running gear consisted of four rubber-tyred bogie wheels each side, which were mounted on bell cranks resisted by compression springs. The turret was offset to the right, and traverse was achieved by shoulder pressure against the machine gun! A further problem was that when the driver's hatch was open, it interfered with the machine-gun traverse, thus the turret was often carried facing to the left.

The Japanese produced a modified version of the Type 94 from 1936 onwards, which incorporated a trailer idler, a lowered drive sprocket and an increased ground contact length for the tracks. The hull was made up of both welded and rivetted parts, and the interior of the driving and fighting compartments, plus the hull, were lined with asbestos panels to give protection against heat radiation.

A diesel version of the Type 94 was built as a prototype. The driver was situated to the left instead of to the right as in earlier variants. Though this tank never went into production, experience gained with it was used in the design of the Type 97 tankette.

TYPE 95

The Type 95 was the best Japanese tank of World War II. It was developed from 1933 to provide a vehicle with speed and mobility for the new mechanised brigades (though steel shortages and a lack of skilled labour meant many never materialized). It had a turret offset to the left, a prominent built-out front machine-gun compartment and two rounded bulges in the centre of the superstructure, which overhung the tracks. The hull and turret were composed of rivetted and bolted plates.

The Type 95 HA-GO had an air-cooled diesel engine that was of an advanced design, and it produced a high output in relation to its weight. Power drive was transmitted to the front sprockets through a sliding gearbox giving four forward gears and one reverse.

There was a modified version of the Type 95, which had a specialized track to improve cross-country performance. The wheels were coupled in pairs by low-attached bogie bolsters of inverted triangular shape. This modification was intended for tanks deployed to the Manchuria theatre.

The Type 98 was a further development of the HA-GO, and ran on six wheels grouped a three bogies each side, with their springing system located inside. Tracks remained front driven, and there was neither hull nor turret rear machine gun, and no cupola above the turret.

SPECIFICATIONS

TYPE 95

Designation: **Light Tank Type 95**	Secondary Armament: **2 x 7.7mm**
Type: **Light Tank**	Engine: **Diesel Six-cylinder**
Length: **4.1m (13.46ft)**	Range: **250km (156 miles)**
Width: **2.05m (6.72ft)**	Speed: **40km/h (25mph)**
Height: **2.28m (7.5ft)**	Fording: **1m (3.25ft)**
Weight: **7534kg (16,576lb)**	Trench Crossing: **2m (6.56ft)**
Crew: **Three**	Armour (hull): **6mm (.23in)**
Main Armament: **37mm**	Armour (turret): **14mm (.55in)**

TYPE 97

SPECIFICATIONS

TYPE 97

Designation: **Medium Tank Type 97**	Secondary Armament: **1 x 7.7mm**
Type: **Medium Tank**	Engine: **Mitsubishi V-12**
Length: **5.5m (18.04ft)**	Range: **210km (131.25 miles)**
Width: **2.33m (7.64ft)**	Speed: **38km/h (23.75mph)**
Height: **2.38m (7.8ft)**	Fording: **1m (3.25ft)**
Weight: **16,087kg (35,392lb)**	Trench Crossing: **2m (6.5ft)**
Crew: **Four**	Armour (hull): **6mm (.23in)**
Main Armament: **57mm**	Armour (turret): **33mm (1.29in)**

Introduced in 1937, the medium tank Type 97, CHI-HA, was one of the best Japanese tanks of World War II, though it was not a match for any US or British main battle tank. The design drew upon European designs, especially Axis, and improvements over other Japanese tanks included a new suspension system. However, as there were still no shock absorbers the tank was a rough ride for the crew. From 1942 onwards the tank underwent a number of changes, including a larger turret mounting a 47mm high-velocity gun. This model was known as the Shinhoto CHI-HA, and production continued until the end of the war.

Japanese tank divisions had two tank brigades, each one equipped with two tank regiments. These were at the heart of the division. There was also a mechanized infantry regiment, though the troops were carried in trucks not halftracks. Other divisional units included a mechanized artillery regiment, antitank battalion, antiaircraft defence unit, a tank reconnaissance unit, a divisional engineer unit, a divisional maintenance unit, a signals transport unit, and a transport unit. Most armoured divisions were stationed in Manchuria and China, such as the 1st Tank Division, first formed as a tank group in December 1941. It ended the war stationed in Japan itself.

LIGHT TANK 7TP

The Polish 7TP began as a development of the Vickers-Armstrong Mk E tank, a number of which were purchased from Great Britain between 1932 and 1934. These tanks appeared in two versions: one with two turrets armed with two machine guns and the other with a single machine gun.

The 7TP was also produced in two versions at first, but later versions were built only as the single-turret variant. The final model was produced until 1939. The final variant had a Vickers suspension and had a special Polish turret (built in Sweden) with a 37mm main gun and coaxial machine gun. A Saurer-designed diesel engine was used in the Polish tank in place of the petrol model used in the earlier Vickers tanks, which helped to maintain a similar performance to that of earlier tanks, although the armour was increased to a maximum of 40mm (1.57in)

Around 170 7TPs of all types were built, and they formed the backbone of Polish armoured formations in September 1939. Although they were outdated when compared to the German panzers, they were in fact better armed than the Panzer Is and IIs which at the time formed the bulk of German armoured strength. The problem was that the Polish Army just did not have enough to defeat the panzers.

SPECIFICATIONS

LIGHT TANK 7TP

Designation: **Light Tank 7TP**	Secondary Armament: **1 x 7.92mm**
Type: **Light Tank**	Engine: **Saurer Diesel Six-cylinder**
Length: **4.57m (15ft)**	Range: **160km (100 miles)**
Width: **2.43m (8ft)**	Speed: **32km/h (20mph)**
Height: **2.13m (7ft)**	Fording: **Unknown**
Weight: **9571kg (21,056lb)**	Trench Crossing: **3.12m (10.23ft)**
Crew: **Three**	Armour (hull): **15mm (.59in)**
Main Armament: **37mm**	Armour (turret): **40mm (1.57in)**

COMBAT CAR M1

SPECIFICATIONS

COMBAT CAR M1

Designation:
Combat Car M1

Type:
Light Tank

Length:
4.45m (14.6ft)

Width:
2.69m (7.75ft)

Height:
2.36m (7.75ft)

Weight:
8877kg (19,530lb)

Crew:
Four

Main Armament:
4 x .5in

Secondary Armament:
None

Engine:
Guiberson 250hp

Range:
112km (70 miles)

Speed:
72km/h (45mph)

Fording:
.9m (3ft)

Trench Crossing:
1.83m (6ft)

Armour (hull):
12.7m (.5in)

Armour (turret):
19mm (.75in)

Produced at the Rock Island Arsenal in 1937, the Combat Car M1 was a development of the Combat Car T1 design for US cavalry units. The Combat Car was in fact a tank built for the cavalry scouting role, but the nomenclature was necessary to bypass the law of Congress of 1920 which made tanks the sole province of the infantry. Individuals such as J. Walter Christie had carried out independent tank development, and his ideas for fast, light tanks with powerful engines and effective suspension would have a profound effect on American tank development.

There were a number of versions of the M1. The M1E2, for example, had a modified engine space and rear bogie moved back some 280mm (11in). The rear of the hull was reshaped for better access and to increase fuel capacity. The Combat Car M1E3 was the M1 fitted with experimental continuous band rubber tracks, and later with rubber tracks. It was built in 1939, but only for trials purposes.

The Combat Car M2 was like the Combat Car M1A1 (which was fitted with constant mesh transmission, turret offset to the right and a radio), but with improved turret and fixed with a Guiberson T1020 diesel engine. A trailing idler was also introduced on this model. The vehicle was redesignated Light Tank M1A1 in 1940.

HEAVY TANK M6

The US Army had considered the need for a heavy tank in 1939, and so the development of the T1 was approved in May 1940. Approval was given to build four variants in February 1941 to test alternative forms of transmission and hull forms. These models were the T1E1, with cast hull and electric drive; T1E2, with cast hull and torque converter drive; T1E3, with welded hull and torque converter drive; and T1E4 with welded hull, four diesel engines and twin Torquematic transmission.

The end result of trials was that the T1E2 was standardised during May 1942 as the Heavy Tank M6, while the T1E3 was standardised as the Heavy Tank M6A1. The only external difference between the two was the welded hull of the latter.

It was planned to produce 5500 M6s, but this was reduced in September 1942 to 115. The US Armored Force had meanwhile been testing the vehicle and found the M6 to be too heavy, undergunned, poorly shaped and having a faulty transmission. Because of these problems and tactical limitations, there was little need for this type of vehicle. As a result, only 40 M6s were built, and these consisted of eight M6s, 12 M6A1s and 20 M6A2s. The series was declared obsolete in late 1944. The US tank that eventually became the answer to the German Panthers and Tigers was the Pershing.

SPECIFICATIONS

HEAVY TANK M6

Designation: **Heavy Tank M6**	Secondary Armament: **4 x .5in**
Type: **Heavy Tank**	Engine: **Wright G-200 800hp**
Length: **7.54m (24.75ft)**	Range: **Unknown**
Width: **3.09m (10.16ft)**	Speed: **35.2km/h (22mph)**
Height: **2.98m (9.8ft)**	Fording: **1.01m (3.3ft)**
Weight: **57,500kg (126,500lb)**	Trench Crossing: **3.04m (10ft)**
Crew: **Six**	Armour (hull): **25.4mm (1in)**
Main Armament: **1 x 3in, 1 x 37mm**	Armour (turret): **82.55mm (3.25in)**

LIGHT TANK M2A2

SPECIFICATIONS

LIGHT TANK M2A2

Designation:
Light Tank M2A2

Type:
Light Tank

Length:
4.14m (13.6ft)

Width:
2.38m (7.83ft)

Height:
2.36m (7.75ft)

Weight:
8681kg (19,100lb)

Crew:
Four

Main Armament:
.5in

Secondary Armament:
2 x .3in

Engine:
Continental Radial 250hp

Range:
100km (62.5 miles)

Speed:
72km/h (45mph)

Fording:
1m (3.28ft)

Trench Crossing:
1.83m (6ft)

Armour (hull):
12.7mm (.5in)

Armour (turret):
19mm (.75in)

Design of the Light Tank T2 was started in 1933, and the pilot model appeared at the Rock Island Arsenal a year later. It was armed with two .3in machine guns, one .5in machine gun and powered by a Continental aircraft engine rated at 260hp. The M2A2 was developed from the T2, being armed like the T2.

The Browning .3in machine gun was designed in 1919 and was a very reliable weapon. It was the standard US tank machine gun throughout World War II. A major advantage was the small hole required in a tank's armour for fitment, though the fabric of its ammunition belt was poor and the feed was not interchangeable between left and right. It had a muzzle velocity of 823m/sec (2700ft/sec) and could fire ball or armour-piercing ammunition.

The Browning .5in was a scaled-up version of the .3in version, and was used primarily in the antiaircraft role. However, it was also used as the main armament of the M2 Combat Car. As well as being the standard antiaircraft machine gun for most US tanks, it served the same purpose on many British tanks.

The M2A2E2 was an M2A2 with modified suspension and thicker armour, while the M2A2E3, which was developed in 1938, had a modified suspension with trailing idler and had a GM diesel engine.

LIGHT TANK M2A4

The M2A4 was one of a line of tanks developed from 1933 onwards and was the first to carry the 37mm gun. This gun was the standard weapon of US light and medium tanks in the period immediately prior to World War II. The M2A4 also had the distinction of being one of the earliest types of fighting vehicle to be supplied to Britain in 1941.

The tank was powered by a Continental aircraft engine which gave a top speed of 59.2km/h (37mph). Its secondary armament, in addition to the turret coaxial .3in Browning, included two further Brownings in sponsons at either side of the driver's and co-driver's positions and another in the glacis plate. Suspension consisted of two two-wheeled bogie units each side, each unit sprung on vertical volute springs. The idler wheel was at the rear, off the ground, and the drive sprocket at the front.

A total of 365 M2A4s was built, and a few of those fought with US forces in the Pacific theatre in 1942 during the early campaigns against the Japanese (the above photograph shows one such vehicle). Those delivered to Great Britain in 1941 – some 40 – were used for Home Defence and training, in which role they were used for familiarizing troops with the similar M3 Light Tank. As such, they provided a crucial service.

SPECIFICATIONS

LIGHT TANK M2A4

Designation:
Light Tank M2A4

Type:
Light Tank

Length:
4.14m (13.6ft)

Width:
2.52m (8.3ft)

Height:
2.36m (7.75in)

Weight:
8681kg (19,100lb)

Crew:
Four

Main Armament:
37mm

Secondary Armament:
1 x .5in, 4 x .3in

Engine:
Continental Radial 250hp

Range:
128km (80 miles)

Speed:
59.2km/h (37mph)

Fording:
1m (3.28ft)

Trench Crossing:
1.83m (6ft)

Armour (hull):
12.7mm (.5in)

Armour (turret):
19mm (.75in)

LIGHT TANK M3

SPECIFICATIONS

LIGHT TANK M3

Designation:
Light Tank M3

Secondary Armament:
3 x .3in

Type:
Light Tank

Engine:
Continental Radial 250hp

Length:
3.29m (14.8ft)

Range:
112.6km (70 miles)

Width:
2.24m (7.34ft)

Speed:
56km/h (35mph)

Height:
2.51m (8.25ft)

Fording:
.9m (3ft)

Weight:
12,523kg (27,552lb)

Trench Crossing:
1.83m (6ft)

Crew:
Four

Armour (hull):
25.4mm (1in)

Main Armament:
37mm

Armour (turret):
38.1mm (1.5in)

Developed from the M2A4, the M3 incorporated improvements found to be necessary from experience with the earlier vehicle. The main change was the introduction of a large trailing idler wheel in place of the idler of the M2A4. This refinement helped to improve stability. As the M3 Stuart came after the outbreak of war, it was able to benefit from information gleaned from combat experience.

Armament remained the same as the M2A4, but it had thicker armour on the front plate and reinforced suspension to take the greater weight. Its hull was welded rather than riveted, and from mid-1941 a gyro-stabilization system was introduced for the main gun, while external fuel tanks were added for additional range.

The M3 entered production in March 1941, and some of the first production models were in the hands of British tank units in the Middle East by August of the same year. The M3 was called Stuart I by the British War Office, and was classed as a light cruiser tank by virtue of its armament and armour. The armament of the M3A1 consisted of a 37mm gun and three .3in Brownings, one coaxial with the main gun, one in the hull front and one as an antiaircraft gun on the turret roof. A variant of the M3 was the T2 mine exploder.

MEDIUM TANK T3

This tank began life as a development of the Christie M1928, a turretless vehicle designed by Christie and built in 1928 by the US Wheel and Track Layer Corporation. The main feature of the vehicle was its ability to run on wheels or tracks by means of the Christie suspension. This consisted of four large weight-carrying wheels on each side, mounted on arms connected to long adjustable springs housed vertically inside the side of the hull. Two of the tanks were sold to the USSR, where they became the basis for the BT series of tanks (see pages 85–87).

The Medium Tank T3 was produced by the same company in 1931, and was accepted into the US Army under the designation T3 Medium Tank. Fitted with a 37mm gun and coaxial .3in machine gun in a fully traversing turret, the original nose gun was eliminated. Four were delivered to the US Cavalry and were redesignated Combat Car T1.

The Medium Tank T3E1 was the designation of two machines contracted by the Polish government, though they eventually entered the US Army as the Poles defaulted on payment. They were similar to the US version, but had a gear drive when operating as wheeled vehicles. The Medium Tank T3E2 had a sloped, widened nose and enlarged turret.

SPECIFICATIONS

MEDIUM TANK T3

Designation:
Medium Tank T3

Type:
Medium Tank

Length:
5.49m (18ft)

Width:
2.41m (7.3ft)

Height:
2.29m (7.5ft)

Weight:
11,200kg (24,640lb)

Crew:
Three

Main Armament:
37mm

Secondary Armament:
1 x .3in

Engine:
Liberty V-12 338hp

Range:
Unknown

Speed:
110.4km/h (69mph)

Fording:
1m (3.28ft)

Trench Crossing:
2.1m (10.7ft)

Armour (hull):
6mm (.23in)

Armour (turret):
13mm (.51in)

M22 LOCUST

SPECIFICATIONS

M22 LOCUST

Designation: **Light Tank T9E1**	Secondary Armament: **1 x .3in**
Type: **Light Tank**	Engine: **Lycoming 162hp**
Length: **3.93m (12.9ft)**	Range: **224km (140 miles)**
Width: **2.2m (7.25ft)**	Speed: **56km/h (35mph)**
Height: **1.72m (5.66ft)**	Fording: **.9m (3ft)**
Weight: **7454kg (16,400lb)**	Trench Crossing: **1.52m (5ft)**
Crew: **Three**	Armour (hull): **19.05mm (.75in)**
Main Armament: **37mm**	Armour (turret): **25.4mm (1in)**

In February 1941 the US Army had expressed a requirement for an air-portable tank. Design studies were submitted by General Motors Corp., the Marmon-Herrington Co. and J. Walter Christie. The Marmon-Herrington design, which employed the Lycoming six-cylinder air-cooled engine and Marmon-Herrington suspension and tracks, was accepted.

The first test model was delivered in the autumn of 1941. The vehicle itself was satisfactory, but there was room for further improvement, and so further design studies of an improved vehicle, the T9E1, were begun in February 1942. These involved the reshaping of the front hull, eliminating the bow machine gun, and removing the turret traverse and gyrostabilizer to decrease weight. The turret and turret basket were removable for air transportation.

The first production models rolled off the production line in March 1943, and some 830 were built between then and February 1944. However, it was never used in action by the US Army, chiefly because the latter lacked an aircraft or glider to transport it. The M22 was supplied to the British, who had the Hamilcar glider to transport it, and it became known as the Locust. It was used by the 6th Airborne Division during the spectacular Rhine crossing in March 1945.

M24 CHAFFEE

Development of the Light Tank T24 began in April 1943 to provide the US Army with an improved vehicle with greater mobility, flotation and accessibility, and also armed with a larger gun than the 37mm weapon used by its predecessors. The first pilot was delivered in October 1943, and following successful trials an order was placed for 5000 vehicles, become the M24 Chaffee in service.

Though it employed the Cadillac powerplant and Hydra-Matic transmission of the M5 series of tanks, it was a redesigned vehicle. The M24 was a low-sleek vehicle with well-sloped armour and large-diameter road wheels sprung on traverse torsion bars. Its main armament was a turret-mounted lightweight 75mm M6 (L/39) gun developed from an aircraft weapon, which employed a space-saving concentric recoil mechanism. It was stabilized in elevation, and the turret had hydraulic power and manual traverse.

The Chaffee was built by two manufacturers – Cadillac and Massey Harris – and by the end of the war a total of 4070 vehicles had been produced in total (a small number being supplied to the British). Used in Europe and the Pacific, the M24 proved itself a good reconnaissance tank with excellent manoeuvrability, which could hold its own in a firefight with the enemy.

SPECIFICATIONS

M24 CHAFFEE

Designation: **Light Tank M24**	Secondary Armament: **2 x .3in, 1 x .5in**
Type: **Light Tank**	Engine: **2 x Cadillac 110hp**
Length: **5.48m (18ft)**	Range: **160km (100 miles)**
Width: **2.95m (9.67ft)**	Speed: **56km/h (35mph)**
Height: **2.46m (8.1ft)**	Fording: **1.02m (3.34ft)**
Weight: **18,409kg (40,500lb)**	Trench Crossing: **2.44m (8ft)**
Crew: **Five**	Armour (hull): **28mm (1.1in)**
Main Armament: **75mm**	Armour (turret): **38mm (1.49in)**

M26 PERSHING

SPECIFICATIONS

M26 PERSHING

Designation:
Heavy Tank T26E3

Secondary Armament:
2 x .3in, 1 x .5in

Type:
Heavy Tank

Engine:
Ford GAF V-8

Length:
6.32m (20.75ft)

Range:
160km (100 miles)

Width:
3.5m (11.5ft)

Speed:
32km/h (20mph)

Height:
2.77m (9.1ft)

Fording:
1.21m (4ft)

Weight:
41,818kg (92,000lb)

Trench Crossing:
2.28m (7.48ft)

Crew:
Five

Armour (hull):
50.8mm (2in)

Main Armament:
90mm

Armour (turret):
101.6mm (4in)

The US Army came to appreciate the need for a heavy tank very late in the war, and it was only in November 1944 that the first 20 prototypes were built. The German Ardennes Offensive of December 1944, during which the inadequacies of the M4 Sherman were revealed once again, prompted the US General Staff to order the immediate despatch of the T26 heavy tank to Europe. The first 20 arrived in January 1945 and were issued to combat units.

The tank's main armament was the 90mm Tank Gun M3. With a muzzle velocity of 1021m/sec (3350ft/sec), it still did not match the German 75mm or 88mm guns that armed the Panthers and Tigers. That said, it had a reasonable performance against enemy armour when firing the armour-piercing, composite rigid round, and its high-explosive round was excellent. The gun was mounted in a turret that had a 360-degree traverse, and the crew consisted of a commander, driver, co-driver, gunner and loader.

Crews found the General Pershing a good fighting vehicle: it was almost a match for the fearsome German Tiger in terms of firepower, and surpassed it with regard to mobility and reliability. A few were sent to Great Britain for trails, but the end of the war in Europe limited the numbers sent.

MEDIUM TANK M3

The M3 was the result of a meeting between the Chief of the Armored Forces and the Ordnance Department. The desire was for the 75mm gun to be mounted in a turret, but insufficient development work had been done on the problem of mounting a large-calibre gun in a revolving turret. However, as experiments had already been carried out on mounting a 75mm pack howitzer in a modified sponson, it was decided that the 75mm gun would be mounted in the right sponson of the new vehicle.

The new vehicle was called the Medium Tank M3, and it had the same Wright radial engine as the M2A1. Its turret and sponson were cast while the rest of hull was riveted, though changes were made in later models. The most important features were the gyrostabilizers for the 75mm and 37mm guns, which meant they could be fired accurately while the vehicle was moving. The A1 version had a cast upper hull, while the A1E1 version was used as a test bed with triple six-cylinder Lycoming engines. The A2 model had an all-welded hull, and the A3 version was fitted with twin General Motors 6-71 diesel engines; the A4 was powered by a Chrysler A-57 Multibank engine; and the A5 was as the M3A3 but had a riveted hull. In all 4924 M3s were built by the time production ceased in August 1942.

SPECIFICATIONS

MEDIUM TANK M3

Designation:
Medium Tank M3

Type:
Medium Tank

Length:
5.63m (18.5ft)

Width:
2.72m (8.92ft)

Height:
3.12m (10.25ft)

Weight:
27,272kg (30,000lb)

Crew:
Six

Main Armament:
75mm

Secondary Armament:
1 x 37mm, 3 x .3in

Engine:
Wright Continental 340hp

Range:
193km (120 miles)

Speed:
41.6km/h (26mph)

Fording:
1.02m (3.3ft)

Trench Crossing:
1.91m (6. 25ft)

Armour (hull):
38.1mm (1.5in)

Armour (turret):
50.8mm (2in)

MEDIUM TANK M4A1

SPECIFICATIONS

MEDIUM TANK M4A1

Designation:
Medium Tank M4A1

Type:
Medium Tank

Length:
5.83m (19.16ft)

Width:
2.6m (8.53ft)

Height:
2.74m (9ft)

Weight:
30,227kg (66,500lb)

Crew:
Five

Main Armament:
75mm

Secondary Armament:
2 x .3in, 1 x .5in

Engine:
Continental 400hp

Range:
160km (100 miles)

Speed:
38.4km/h (24mph)

Fording:
.9m (3ft)

Trench Crossing:
2.26m (7.41ft)

Armour (hull):
25.4mm (1in)

Armour (turret):
50.8mm (2in)

Of the tanks that saw service in World War II, the M4 Sherman was probably the most important, and certainly most widely produced, of all tanks to see service with the Allies in the war. In 1941 it was decided to use the M3 lower hull, powerplant, transmission and running gear for a new tank, with a redesigned upper hull mounting a central turret armed with a 75mm gun. A prototype was completed in September 1941, and initial production was placed at 2000 per month. The first models saw combat at El Alamein in October 1942, and from then on it became the backbone of Allied armoured strength. In all, over 40,000 were built.

The Sherman was reliable, easy to maintain, rugged and highly mobile. Though it lacked the firepower of German and Soviet tanks, it was up-gunned and up-armoured throughout its life. The A1, standardised in December 1941, had a cast hull designed to present less flat surfaces to a direct hit from any angle. It also had a three-piece differential housing and vision slots in the front armour. Later production models of the A1 had periscopes replacing the vision slots for the driver and appliqué armour attached to the turret.

The Sherman continued to serve as a frontline tank after World War II: the Israelis used them to great effect in their early conflicts in the Middle East.

MEDIUM TANK M4A3

Having a welded hull and cast turret, the A3 was powered by a 500hp Ford engine. The early production model was equipped with the M34 gun mount, vision slots in the front armour and a cast, one-piece round-nosed differential housing. The vision slots were replaced on later models by periscopes for the driver, and this model was also fitted with sand shields. The last version of the A3 was equipped with the 75mm gun in an M34A1 gun mount, a vision cupola for the tank commander, and placed a small oval hatch over the loader's position.

Other features of this vehicle included a 47-degree front armour plate on the hull, larger driver's doors and a cast one-piece, sharp-nosed differential housing. Some versions were fitted with 75mm ammunition racks which had liquid-filled containers on either side to prevent fire in case the side of the vehicle was pierced. As this arrangement was known as "wet stowage", models fitted with this feature were known as M4A3W.

The first up-gunning of the Sherman involved replacing the 75mm gun with the 76mm model, which was a high-velocity weapon designed to knock out all enemy tanks then in service. Unfortunately, its antitank performance was inferior to the guns mounted by German Tiger and Panther tanks.

SPECIFICATIONS

MEDIUM TANK M4A3

Designation: **Medium Tank M4A3**	Secondary Armament: **2 x .3in, 1 x .5in**
Type: **Medium Tank**	Engine: **Ford GAA-III 500hp**
Length: **6m (19.66ft)**	Range: **160km (100 miles)**
Width: **2.6m (8.53ft)**	Speed: **40km/h (25mph)**
Height: **2.74m (9ft)**	Fording: **.9m (3ft)**
Weight: **31,136kg (68,500lb)**	Trench Crossing: **2.26m (7.41ft)**
Crew: **Five**	Armour (hull): **25.4mm (1in)**
Main Armament: **75mm**	Armour (turret): **50.8mm (2in)**

MINE EXPLODER T3

SPECIFICATIONS

MINE EXPLODER T3

Designation:
Mine Exploder T3

Type:
Anti-mine Tank

Length:
8.23m (27ft)

Width:
3.5m (11.48ft)

Height:
2.74m (9ft)

Weight:
31,818kg (70,000lb)

Crew:
Five

Main Armament:
75mm

Secondary Armament:
2 x .3in. 1 x .5in

Engine:
Ford GAA V-8 500hp

Range:
62km (100 miles)

Speed:
46km/h (28.75mph)

Fording:
.9m (3ft)

Trench Crossing:
2.26m (7.5ft)

Armour (hull):
25.4mm (1in)

Armour (turret):
76mm (2.99in)

The problem of having to deal with enemy mines, especially when having to breach heavily defended Axis positions, resulted in a number of special variants of the Sherman fitted with rollers, flails and plunger rods. The Mine Exploder T1 was developed in 1943 and put into limited production. It consisted of two roller units, each of five 3m- (10ft-) diameter steel discs driven by a roller chain from the tank's drive sprocket.

The Mine Exploder T1E4 was developed as a more manoeuvrable version, and consisted of 16 discs, each of 1219mm (48in) diameter, mounted in a single heavy frame unit which was driven in front of the tank.

The T3 was developed in 1943 and based on the British Scorpion flail device, which had proved to be a success and relatively simple to manufacture. It consisted of two booms extending forward from the tank with a rotating shaft fitted with chains to beat the ground as the tank advanced. Power for the rotor was obtained from an auxiliary engine.

The T8 was a curious vehicle, having a series of vertical plunger rods mounted on a pivoted frame in front of the tank. It was geared to strike the ground as the tank moved forward, and thus detonate any mines in its path. The device was tested in 1944, but only one pilot model was built.

SHERMAN FLAMETHROWER

Flamethrowers have traditionally exerted a powerful psychological effect on opponents. It was therefore logical that the Americans should develop a flamethrower version of their main battle tank. In fact, the US Army developed a number of flamethrower tanks. The M4-3 was a standard Sherman that could be fitted with a flamethrower kit that was installed in place of the bow machine gun, with a 22-gallon fuel tank situated in the right sponson.

The POA-CWS 75-HI Flamethrower was a Pacific theatre improvisation. It used a US Navy Mk I flamethrower with the projector tube fitted inside the barrel of a 75mm M3 gun. Some 62 vehicles were thus converted, and found much work in incinerating stubborn Japanese defenders during the Pacific War.

The Anti-Personnel Tank Projector E1 was developed in 1945, and consisted of four special flamethrowers that were mounted externally on Shermans to protect them from enemy troops attempting to place bombs or magnetic mines on the vehicles. Each unit was controlled electrically from within the vehicle by a push-button switch. They could be fired singly or simultaneously. The final flamethrower Sherman was the T33, which carried the flame fuel and propellant gas inside the vehicle.

SPECIFICATIONS

FLAMETHROWER

Designation: Flamethrower Tank	**Secondary Armament:** 2 x .3in, 1 x .5in
Type: Medium Tank	**Engine:** Ford GAA-III 500hp
Length: 6m (19.66ft)	**Range:** 160km (100 miles)
Width: 2.6m (8.53ft)	**Speed:** 40km/h (25mph)
Height: 2.74m (9ft)	**Fording:** .9m (3ft)
Weight: 31,136kg (68,500lb)	**Trench Crossing:** 2.26m (7.41ft)
Crew: Five	**Armour (hull):** 25.4mm (1in)
Main Armament: 75mm	**Armour (turret):** 50.8mm (2in)

TANK DESTROYER M10

SPECIFICATIONS

TANK DESTROYER M10

Designation:
Gun Motor Carriage M10

Type:
Tank Destroyer

Length:
6.83m (22.5ft)

Width:
3.05m (10ft)

Height:
2.57m (8.4ft)

Weight:
29,937kg (65,861lb)

Crew:
Five

Main Armament:
76mm

Secondary Armament:
1 x .5in

Engine:
General Motors 375hp x 2

Range:
322km (200 miles)

Speed:
51km/h (32mph)

Fording:
.9m (3ft)

Trench Crossing:
2.26m (7.5ft)

Armour (hull):
12mm (.47in)

Armour (turret):
37mm (1.46in)

Before World War II, the US Army had devoted a great deal of thought to defeating large, fast-moving enemy tank formations. The answer it formulated was the employment of large numbers of tank destroyers. The Gun Motor Carriage M10 was the product of this concept. It was based on the M4A3 chassis and mounted the 76mm M7 (L/52) gun in a low, open-topped turret that had a 360-degree traverse. The five-man crew consisted of commander, driver and the three servers of the gun.

Production of the M10 began in September 1942 and had finished by December of the same year. By then some 7000 vehicles had been produced. In the field the concept of separate tank-destroyer battalions proved ineffective, and thus most M10s were used for offensive purposes to support attacks. The M10 continued in service until the end of the war, but by then had become obsolete. A few entered British service, being designated "3in SP Wolverine".

The M36 was a development of the M10, being armed with a 90mm gun in place of the smaller weapon in a larger turret. This vehicle was an excellent tank destroyer, and true to the original US Army concept, and could take on the Tigers and Panthers of the enemy on an equal footing.

BT-2

In December 1930, the Soviet Union purchased two US Christie M1928 convertible tanks (see page 75), which became known in Soviet service as the BT-1. The first Soviet prototypes, known as the BT-2, were completed in October 1931 and took part in the Moscow parade on 7 November of that year.

The BT series of medium tanks were designed as fast vehicles undertaking the traditional cavalry role of exploitation. Production of the BT-2 began in 1932 and was ended the following year, by which time 4000 vehicles had been built. The tank was fast, but was unreliable and was cramped for the three-man crew. The tank did have some interesting features, such as the capability of running either on its tracks or on its road wheels as required. Armament was satisfactory for its intended role, with a 37mm main gun and a ball-mounted machine gun. Amazingly, this tank was still in service in 1940.

The BT-3 was a modified version of the BT-2, with solid disc wheels in place of the spoked type of earlier vehicles. It was also up-gunned with a 45mm gun. The BT-4 was a prototype with hull features similar to the BT-3 but with twin turrets replacing the single turret. The major problem with the BT-2 was its mechanical unreliability, a problem never entirely solved.

SPECIFICATIONS

BT-2

Designation: **BT-2**	Secondary Armament: **1 x 7.62mm**
Type: **Medium Tank**	Engine: **400hp**
Length: **5.48m (18ft)**	Range: **300km (187 miles)**
Width: **2.23m (7.33ft)**	Speed: **72km/h (45mph)**
Height: **1.92m (6.33ft)**	Fording: **1m (3.28ft)**
Weight: **11,200kg (24,640lb)**	Trench Crossing: **2.1m (10.7ft)**
Crew: **Three**	Armour (hull): **6mm (.23in)**
Main Armament: **37mm**	Armour (turret): **13mm (.51in)**

BT-5

SPECIFICATIONS

BT-5

Designation:
BT-5

Secondary Armament:
1 x 7.62mm

Type:
Medium Tank

Engine:
Type M5 350hp

Length:
5.48m (18ft)

Range:
200km (125 miles)

Width:
2.23m (7.33ft)

Speed:
70km/h (43.75mph)

Height:
2.2m (7.25ft)

Fording:
1m (3.28ft)

Weight:
11,709kg (25,760lb)

Trench Crossing:
1m (3.28ft)

Crew:
Three

Armour (hull):
6mm (.23in)

Main Armament:
45mm

Armour (turret):
13mm (.51in)

Problems with the BT-2 came to a head during the November 1932 Moscow parade, when two of the vehicles broke down during the display (the comments of the watching Soviet leaders are not recorded!). This prompted two new designs intended to improve the tank's reliability and battlefield potency – the BT-3 and BT-4 – but they were both rejected. The BT-5 was a major production model with an enlarged cylindrical turret, 45mm main gun, a new engine, improved vision devices and a stronger suspension.

The 45mm Tank Gun M32 was an excellent weapon for its time. With a muzzle velocity of 760m/sec (2492ft/sec), it had good armour penetration. However, as tank armour increased in thickness it became outclassed and was eventually replaced in Soviet tanks by the 76.2mm gun.

The BT-5(V) was a commander's tank. It was identical to the BT-5 apart from a frame round the turret and the provision of a radio in the rear turret overhang. The BT-5A was an artillery version of the tank, and mounted the 76.2mm Model 27/32 howitzer in the T-28 turret. Around 65 BT-5s fought in the Spanish Civil War, and they showed themselves to be superior to the German Panzer I and the Italian tankettes in service with the Nationalist forces.